SERVE CHILLED

SUFFOLK ELEGANCE

WINE FROM GRAPES GROWN AT
THE HANSON VINEYARD
IPSWICH ENGLAND

MADE AND
BOTTLED AT
THE VINEYARD

HORAM MANOR

Estate Bottled
Table Wine
70cl

Merrydown Wine Co Ltd Horam Heathfield, East Sussex
Produce of the United Kingdom

PILTON MANOR

Riesling Sylvaner

TABLE WINE

Vineyard replanted, originally established by the
abbots of Glastonbury C.1189. Estate grown and bottled at
The Pilton Manor Vineyard, Pilton, Somerset, England
Min. Contents 70cl.

LANGHAM

MÜLLER THURGAU

White Table Wine

Grown by
LANGHAM FRUIT FARMS LTD
Langham, Colchester, Essex

Produce of England   Vol 70cl

Wine from the Mendips

WRAXALL

Table Wine

Wells
Glastonbury   WRAXALL
                Fosse Way
        Castle Cary

GROWN BY A.S.HOLMES AT WRAXALL VINEYARD, SHEPTON MALLET, SOMERSET.
PRODUCE OF UNITED KINGDOM   MINIMUM CONTENTS 70CLS

**CHICKERING
RIVANER**

White Table Wine

produce of Suffolk,   70cl.   bottled by
UNITED KINGDOM   Cherrybank Estates
                                 Oxley, IPSWICH

**Elmham
Jubilee Cask**

Medium-dry
White Table Wine

Produced and Estate Bottled
by R.S.Don Wine Growers
at North Elmham Norfolk England

1976

TYTHERLEY

DRY WHITE
ENGLISH TABLE WINE

Bottled by the producer J.R.M. Donald
The Garden House, West Tytherley, Salisbury, Wilts.

PRODUCE OF UK

e 70cl

PENSHURST

Estate Bottled by the Producer

ENGLISH
DRY WHITE TABLE
WINE
70 cl

**MARRIAGE
HILL**

*White Table
Wine · 70cls*   Grown and Bottled by M. Waterfield
                at Marriage Farm, Wye, Kent, U.K.

KIRBY

Grown in the Coombe Valley
by JOHN ASTOR
Kirby House Inkpen Berks UK

Bottled by the Merrydown Wine Company   70cl

ISLE OF THE
WATERHOUSE

hendred

medium dry white wine

A MEDIUM DRY WHITE TABLE WINE PRODUCED FROM
REICHENSTEINER GRAPES IN THE VALE OF THE WHITE HORSE

RENISHAW

RENISHAW HALL
DERBYSHIRE

WHITE WINE

Grown and bottled on the estate
by Reresby Sitwell
at Renishaw Hall near Sheffield

CUCKMERE

ENGLISH WHITE TABLE WINE

70cl.

The New
English
Vineyard

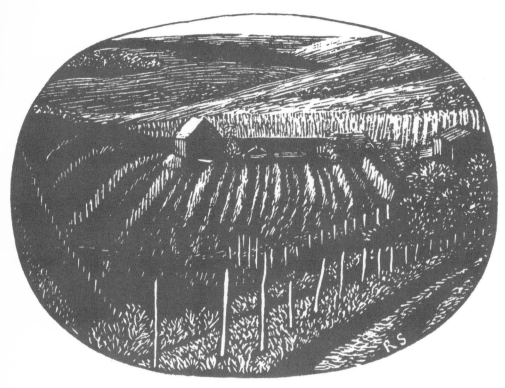

Wood-engraving by Reynolds Stone
from the wine label of Breaky Bottom Vineyard, Sussex,
by kind permission of the owner, Peter Hall

JOANNA SMITH

The New  *English Vineyard*

*A PRACTICAL GUIDE TO GROWING VINES
AND MAKING WINE IN BRITAIN & IRELAND*
with a gazetteer of British vineyards
and their wines

Sidgwick & Jackson
London

First published in Great Britain by
Sidgwick & Jackson Limited
Copyright © 1979 Joanna Smith
Line drawings by Deborah Jane Kartun

ISBN 0 283 98519 4

Printed in Great Britain by
A. Wheaton & Company Limited, Exeter, Devon, England
for Sidgwick & Jackson Limited
1 Tavistock Chambers, Bloomsbury Way
London WC1A 2SG

She considereth a field, and buyeth it: with the fruit of her hands she planteth a vineyard.

(PROVERBS 31 : 16)

Let us get up early to the vineyards; let us see if the vine flourish, whether the tender grape appear.

(THE SONG OF SOLOMON 7 : 12)

Contents

Acknowledgements

Much help has been received from numbers of people and particularly from:

Mrs Jill O'Brien and Mr Tony Heath, both of the Agricultural Development and Advisory Service

Mr Jack Ward and the staff of the Merrydown Wine Company

Mr Derek Pearman of Loftus

Mr Bob Farrar of Wye College

Mr and Mrs Graham Barrett, The Vineyard, Cricks Green, Essex

Mr Bill Carcary, Hambledon Vineyard, Hampshire

Mr Christopher Clark, Cherrybank Estates, Suffolk

M. Florian Geiger, France

Major and Mrs Colin Gillespie, Wootton Vineyard, Somerset

Mr and Mrs Nigel Godden, Pilton Manor Vineyard, Somerset

Mr Peter Hall, Breaky Bottom Vineyard, Sussex

Mr Eric Hanson, Hanson Vineyard, Suffolk

Mr A. S. Holmes and his son, Mr D. J. Holmes, Wraxall Vineyard, Somerset

Mr Eamon Kelly, An Foras Talúntais, Ballygagin, Ireland

Mr Michael O'Callaghan, Longueville House, Ireland

Messrs Ian and Andrew Paget, Chilsdown Vineyard, West Sussex

Mr N. Poulter and Mr R. H. Gibbons, Cranmore Vineyard, Isle of Wight

Mr Richard Sherwood, Llanrystyd Vineyard, Wales

Mr Reresby Sitwell, Renishaw Hall, Derbyshire

Mr Stephen Skelton, Spots Farm Vineyard, Kent

Mrs Pamela Smith, Flexerne Vineyard, East Sussex

Mr Bernard Theobald, Westbury Farm, Berkshire

M. Vincent Thierry, France

Dr Idris Thomas, Wern Dêg Vineyard, Wales

Mr Michael Waterfield, Marriage Hill, Kent

Mr Neville Weale, Maryville Vineyards, Ireland

Mr Bob Westphal, Penshurst Vineyard, Kent
Dr Ivor Williams, Harefield Vineyard, Kent

and hundreds of members of the English Vineyards Association who have supplied information on their vines and wines. I owe a large debt for investigations on behalf of the book in Ireland, Wales, Scotland and France, to:

Mrs Marion Drescher, Mrs Mary Feeny, Miss Maxine Feifer, Mr William Montgomery.

I am grateful to the following for allowing me to reproduce their photographs in this book:

Basil Ambrose, Cavendish Manor; Graham Barrett, Felsted; Ray Barrington-Brock; British Farmer and Stockbreeder; British Tourist Authority; Harold Chapman; C. Clive-Ponsonby-Fane, Brympton d'Evercy; Jayne Diggory; English Vineyards Association; Mary Evans Picture Library; Fairfields Fruit Farms Ltd; Farmers' Weekly; Fox Photos; Charles Gordon, Hoe; R. Greenwood, New Hall; A. G. D. Heath; Charles de Jaeger; Keystone Press; Gail Lazarus; National Farmers' Union; Thelma Shumsky; Kenneth Scowen; Pamela Smith, Flexerne; Bernard Theobald, Westbury Farm; John Topham Picture Library; Jack Ward, OBE, Merrydown Wine Co; The Welsh Folk Museum; Western Mail and Echo; G. Maxwell-Wilkins; Trevor Wood.

I must also thank Major Colin Gillespie of Wootton Vines who most generously allowed his vineyard and winery to be photographed throughout the year; Robert Carrier for allowing me to print his lovely recipe for pot roast pork with grapes; Deborah Kartun for her painstaking, accurate and decorative drawings; Jillian O'Brien of ADAS, who found time to read the text and make many helpful suggestions; Mr Tony Heath for kindly consenting to read the proofs. Above all I must thank Patricia Evans for deciphering my handwriting, typing and retyping the text, extracting information from busy vineyard owners, driving me to one vineyard after another and, as one vine-grower rightly pointed out, 'doing all the work'.

Introduction

While writing *The New English Vineyard* I have met many people who grow vines up and down the country on a scale which varies from the kitchen garden to the full-sized commercial vineyard, and have also accumulated practical experience in our own vineyard and in the vineyards of others. The result, I hope, is a complete picture of how vineyards are run, illustrated from as many types of vineyard as possible, small and large, and from all the vine-growing regions of Britain. The histories of various individual vineyards and their owners will be interesting to those who are considering taking the plunge, while the gazetteer of British vineyards will help them in their local investigations. Having approached the subject with a completely open mind, I am now convinced that there is a future for vine-growing in this country, both for amateurs, for whom it is a fascinating hobby, and for professionals, for whom it can provide a life which is pioneering, absorbing and even, in some cases, financially rewarding.

In this book, I am going to refer to wine produced from grapes grown in the British Isles as English wine rather than British wine, even though wine is being produced in Wales, Ireland and the Channel Islands, as well as in England. Unfortunately the term 'British' wine has always been used of wines manufactured in Britain from imported grape juice. Such wines are now called 'made' wines under EEC regulations, and are usually fortified wines which aim to taste like sherry or port. Sometimes they are labelled 'tonic' wines. Years ago I was in a bar with a friend, who, surprised to see a bottle labelled 'British wine', asked where the grapes had come from. The barman gave him a sour look. 'British wine', he said, 'don't need no grapes.'

So I think that growers in the rest of the British Isles will forgive me for including their wines with the English wines, which definitely do need grapes and are made entirely from grapes grown in this country.

Metric equivalents have been provided for Imperial measurements throughout the book, with the exception of hectares which are so rarely used. For the metrically minded, 1 hectare equals $2\frac{1}{2}$ acres.

CHAPTER ONE

❧ *Why Plant a Vineyard?*

Wine is one of life's most lasting pleasures. There can be no more friendly sight than a bottle of wine on the dinner table with the glasses gleaming beside it, no more delectable smell than the fragrance from its contents, while in the kitchen, wine is indispensable for the subtle and ancient skills of cooking. The ambivalent attitude towards wine in these until recently deprived islands is rapidly disappearing—except of course in government circles. Iago summed it up: 'Good wine is a good familiar creature if it be well-used; exclaim no more against it.'

Planting a vineyard is an adventure and nowhere is this more true than in the British Isles, where vine-growers are still learning after more than thirty years of experiment and every grower is something of a pioneer. The amount of research that is being done in Britain is tiny and it is being done on a shoe-string. Nevertheless, grapes are growing, wine is being made, sold and enjoyed, and every year more people plant vines.

The reasons for this cannot be primarily economic. Some commercial growers are undoubtedly making money, but most would admit that the sales of wine alone, without profitable sidelines which are a feature of several vineyards, would not bring riches, while the many amateur winemakers who grow grapes in their gardens would be far better off financially making wine from elderberries.

People grow grapes because they want to. Their reward is the incomparable subtlety and aroma of wine with its infinite variety from year to year and from vineyard to vineyard.

A vineyard is a beautiful thing. The regular lines and satisfying order, the luxuriant foliage, changing through the year from a tender bronze to the vivid green of summer and the autumn scarlet and gold, the hanging clusters of grapes, make a vineyard an ornament to any landscape. In the garden, vines can transform a fence or a wall, they can be grown down a path on trellises or be trained over a too-sunny space to give shade. All this and wine too: no wonder people want to grow vines!

An encouraging precedent for British growers is the case of New Zealand, so similar in its climate. There, the first grapes were planted in 1819 by a missionary, the Reverend Samuel Marsden. A government research station was set up in 1898 and this came to specialize in vines, but not very much happened for the next decades apart from the establishment of a few small commercial vineyards. The Second World War provided the stimulus for a rapid expansion which has continued, protected by import controls. Demand has outstripped supply, particularly for the finer wines, but New Zealand now produces most of the wine it consumes. I am told that New Zealand wine is very good but you have to go to New Zealand to taste it, for the New Zealanders drink it all themselves.

Here in Britain the government has so far done little to help the infant English wine industry. Indeed there seems to be a feeling that wine drinkers are hedonistic upper-class parasites as opposed to beer drinkers, who are assumed to be honest proletarians. So wine is taxed heavily, whether it is produced at home or abroad. This is serious for the commercial vineyards, but is a great incentive for do-it-yourself winemaking, which is not taxed. There may well be wine lakes in France and Italy, but these will not be allowed to irrigate Britain without a large contribution to the Chancellor's coffers. Nor does everybody like the thought of drinking the cheaper wines. It has been publicly stated that some of the wines from the more dubious areas of Italy contain no grapes at all (though this is illegal, of course) while there have been scandals in France over contamination from asbestos and fibreglass. Nevertheless, the consumption of wine in Britain rises every year. Those who like to drink wine regularly, but cannot afford to buy it, make their own, and they save between £700 and £1500 every year. Inflation has brought the great home winemaking boom.

Simultaneously, recession has encouraged the establishment of commercial vineyards. To people with ever poorer job prospects, bringing ever more meagre rewards, vineyards seem to offer a pleasant life with a comparatively good return on a small acreage. The sort of people who would have put their savings into a chicken farm or smallholding in the thirties are now much attracted by vine-growing.

This is not to say that it is easy to make a good living out of a commercial vineyard. Mrs Barrett, the Secretary of the English Vineyards

Association, who with her husband has successfully built up a winery and a paying vineyard told me: 'People don't seem to realize that they will not have any income at all from a vineyard for the first four years, and it may well be longer than that before they have a good crop and manage to make a good wine—and then they have to sell it!' Yet the appeal of those rows of vines and clusters of grapes remains.

There seem to be four groups of people who find it quite impossible to resist: the rich, who, having a good income from other sources, derive considerable tax advantages from the initial costs and running expenses of a vineyard; people who have retired early, perhaps from the army or the navy, with some capital to invest and a new life to make; amateurs who want to make wine they can be proud of from their own vines in their own gardens; and those adventurous people who are simply determined to do it and make a living from it, whatever the difficulties may be.

The challenge of producing grapes at the very limits of their range, of proving the experts wrong, appeals to a great many people. In other vine-growing countries, it has been assumed that vines cannot be grown in areas where there are less than 1000 day-degrees between May and October (day-degrees being a measure of total heat above 10 °C – the temperature below which vines will not grow). In the United Kingdom, only East Malling Research Station in Kent topped 1000 day-degrees in 1976, which was a very hot year, but other weather stations at Wattisham (Suffolk), Writtle (Essex), Wye (Kent), Efford (Hampshire) and Long Ashton (near Bristol) did not reach 1000 day-degrees even in 1976. Over the last eight years, apart from 1976, the best has been between 800 and 900 day-degrees. In poor years less than 500 day-degrees has been recorded occasionally. To sum up, very seldom do we reach temperatures regarded on the Continent as the minimum necessary for vines, and sometimes we have less than half the desirable minimum, yet the proof is in the drinking. A million bottles of wine a year are produced from commercial vineyards in the United Kingdom.

Grapes have been grown out of doors for centuries in Britain and the tradition has been kept alive, though on a small scale, in spite of climate, pests and disease.* For many centuries, the most common alcoholic drink of this country has been beer or ale. Country house-wives have also made their own potent country wines from flowers,

---

* See page 149 for a short history of vines and wines in Britain.

herbs, vegetables and wild berries. Yet the vine has never been forgotten. Wine is a central symbol in the Christian religion; it baptizes
our ships (a tradition which goes back to the libations of the Greeks);
no celebration or party seems complete without it; monks bordered
their manuscripts with the vine branches and tendrils which also twine
over the engraved glass windows of many a Victorian pub. Indeed,
several pubs in which wine has not been drunk in living memory have
a bunch of grapes as an inn sign.

The twentieth-century vine-grower will want to know what yields
he can expect from his vines. Yields vary widely, but an average yield
of 4 tons per acre, through good years and bad, is perfectly possible. In
efficient Luxembourg, farmers expect a yield of 8 tons per acre; surely
in Britain we can manage to do at least half as well. In at least one
English vineyard, Flexerne in East Sussex, the average yield over the
past three years has been 5 tons per acre. One ton of grapes gives
approximately nine hundred bottles of wine. For the home winemaker
this means that if one-eighth of an acre can be planted with about 270
vines (1.2 m/4 feet apart and 1.5 m/5 feet between the rows) he should
harvest, on average, 500 kg (10 cwt) of grapes, once the vines have
fully matured, and this is enough to make 450 bottles of wine. It can
be done.

CHAPTER TWO

✿ *Planning*

A vine will keep you waiting for three years before it can be allowed to crop and will take five years to come into full bearing, but then it may live for a hundred years or more. The vines of Château-Ausone in the Saint-Émilion district of Bordeaux are over one hundred years old and are still productive. Well sited vines could stock the cellars of the children and grandchildren of the men who planted them, or could prove a valuable asset, were the house to be sold. So planning and preparation are very important.

Vines will grow just about anywhere. They are very hardy and vigorous. They will put up well with hard winters and summer drought, but they will not give of their best in cool British summers unless they are in a sunny, fairly sheltered place, not too high above sea level. It seems that grapes will not ripen further north than Lincolnshire without the protection of cloches, although in Lancashire some early ripening grapes do well against a wall. With the help of cloches it is possible to ripen grapes as far north as Edinburgh.

There are commercial vineyards in Jersey, Cornwall, Devon, Somerset, Avon, Wiltshire, Hampshire, the Isle of Wight, Berkshire, Gloucestershire, Oxfordshire, Bedfordshire, Surrey, Sussex, Kent, Essex, Suffolk, Norfolk, Lincolnshire, Derbyshire, Staffordshire, Leicestershire, Cambridgeshire, Herefordshire, Worcestershire, Glamorgan and Dyfed. Most of these vineyards are south-east of a line drawn from the west of Hampshire to the Wash. Although Wales and the West Country are milder than the east, they are more humid and this is not ideal for grapes, although there are several fine West Country vineyards.

There are vineyards on all types of soil, from heavy clay to the most uncompromising chalk, so there are few people in Britain who could not consider growing vines, although in colder areas the vines would need protection.

Vines in the small garden

The amateur vine-grower and winemaker has some distinct advantages over the man who does it commercially. He can afford to take the risk of cutting down on the spraying programme, can plant an adventurous choice of varieties, can experiment with different ways of pruning and training vines and can exploit the most minute micro-climates by planting the choicest vines in sunny sheltered spots in his garden. His planning must take into account the space available for vines and the requirements of the grower. Where space is very limited, the obvious site for a vine is against a sunny wall or fence. Very heavy crops can be obtained from a healthy vine with the help of some extra warmth and protection.

To give an extreme example: under glass, the famous vine at Hampton Court Palace has been known to give 2272 bunches of grapes in one season, weighing a total of 900 kg (18 cwt). The Hampton Court vine is over two hundred years old and is gigantic, so I do not mean to imply that one vine planted now could do as well in a few years' time. Nevertheless, a wall-grown vine, even without glass protection, can be very generous and the home winemaker should do well with five or six plants.

The Merrydown Wine Company has three wall-trained vines at its premises at Horam in East Sussex. In good years these three vines between them produce over 50 kg (1 cwt) of grapes, enough to make 32 litres (7 gallons) of wine.

One of the loveliest ways to grow a vine is to train it on a frame over a sunny terrace or patio, where it will provide a green and beautiful shade for hot sunny days, considerately delaying coming into leaf until May so as to allow the sun to warm you in the spring, and removing itself as the heat and light decline in autumn. The bunches of grapes hang down most decoratively from the branches, but it might be wise to choose one of the later ripening varieties and not those precocious vines that ripen in August and would attract wasps to where you are sitting.

It is very much easier to make good wine in large quantities, so the home winemaker who can produce 70 kg (150 lb) of grapes, which will give 45 litres (10 gallons) of wine, is well placed to make wine of fine quality.

A family-sized vineyard

In the rather larger garden, vines could be grown not only on walls but on pergolas, down garden paths or, like other soft fruits, in the kitchen garden, grown in rows on a wire trellis, like raspberries or loganberries. A hundred vines, planted about 0.9 m (3 feet) apart, could give 250 kg (550 lb) of grapes to make 240 bottles or as much wine as the average family might drink in a year. For an account of a kitchen-garden vineyard (Mr Westphal's garden at Penshurst) see page 125.

On this scale, more than one variety can be grown and the wine-maker can experiment with blending or with making wine from different varieties in batches. The costs of setting up a small vineyard such as this need not be high, for machinery will not be necessary and second-hand materials could be used for posts, wires and fencing.

A commercial vineyard

If a paddock or field is available, then it would be well worth con-sidering planting a commercial vineyard. To make a living out of a vineyard, most people would agree that it should extend to 5 acres or more, but if the vineyard is to be combined with other enterprises then it could be much smaller than this. Mr Michael Waterfield, at Wye in Kent, has a vineyard of only $1\frac{1}{2}$ acres. Here he spends two or three days a week tending his vines and the rest of the week he manages his restaurant, the Wife of Bath, at Wye. The restaurant provides an ideal outlet for his wine.

A commercial vineyard (unless it is on the Geneva Double Curtain system, see pages 53–5) cannot cost less than £1000 per acre to establish assuming that the grower does all the work himself and makes no allowance for his labour; with hired labour and new equipment the cost would be very much higher. But, if successful, the grower should be able to produce on average 3000 to 4000 bottles per acre—up to 5000 or 6000 bottles in a good year. Mr Ian Paget, of Chilsdown Vineyard in West Sussex, estimated that the maximum potential yield from his vineyard would be 80,000 bottles, or just under 8000 bottles per acre, which at present fetches £2 or more per bottle. The income from a successful vineyard is not to be sneezed at.

If it is intended to make the wine at the vineyard (and in the end this is infinitely more satisfactory than having it made elsewhere) then the cost of establishing a vineyard increases sharply. In fact the winery

would probably cost far more than the vineyard. A successful grower
with a good enterprise should be able to justify the capital expenditure
on the winery.

Few vineyards are commercially viable on the income from sales of
wine alone, but there are other ways of making a vineyard pay,
notably through tourism and the sale of vines. One vineyard, Cranmore
on the Isle of Wight, sold 60,000 vines to the public in 1978 alone.
Another vineyard in Jersey expects to receive 20,000 visitors in a season.
Now no vine-grower likes to depend on such sidelines for his income,
but most recognize that they can help to cover the costs of setting up a
vineyard while the vines are not yet in full production, while experience
is being gained and the wine is making its reputation. Building on this,
the efficient grower and talented winemaker have a great opportunity.

Judging by the experience of the USA, as domestic water supplies
become more heavily laced with unpalatable chemicals, other drinks,
including wine, become more and more popular. Wine consumption
is rising rapidly in the United Kingdom but is still very low compared
to other countries and many shrewd farmers are planting vines, convinced that the market is growing fast.

While researching for this book I have met a great many commercial
growers. Not one appeared to regret the decision to plant a vineyard,
whatever the difficulties might have been.

CHAPTER THREE

✿ *Choosing a Site for Vines*

Wall-trained vines

A vine will grow and fruit very well on a sunny wall. South-facing walls are the best, but walls facing south-east or south-west are also suitable. The vine can be trained to accommodate the doors and windows of a house and can be allowed to grow to a very large size, though it must be correctly pruned. If a vine is allowed to grow with only minimal pruning, then it will grow right up to the eaves of a house, look splendidly decorative and fruit copiously, but the fruit will be of poor quality and will not make such good wine as that from a vine which has been pruned.

A wall-trained vine can be trained into almost any shape to suit the space available to it. It could be tall and thin, with the fruit borne on spurs from the main stem; it could be spread out in a fan or bear fruit on spurs from a grid of horizontal arms, or be trained low, perhaps against a low wall or under a row of windows. Therefore almost any sunny wall would be suitable for vines. The vines should be planted at a minimum of 1.8 m (6 feet) apart and at least 300 mm (1 foot) out from the wall.

Vines in the open

The same principles apply whether twenty-five or five thousand vines are to be planted. Once away from the protection of a wall, vines will only give of their best if the site is carefully chosen. The essential requirement is that the site should be as open and sunny as possible. Trees which shade the vines should be removed. A sheltered position is good, but some movement of air is desirable, as fresh air moving through the leaves will help to discourage moulds and mildews. Hollows and valley bottoms should be avoided in areas subject to late frosts, but fortunately frosts are rare at the time when they would do most damage to the vines, that is in May and June.

Ripening dates become later by about five days for every 30 m (100 feet) one climbs above sea level. Ripening also tends to be earlier in the west of the country than in the east. The less favourable the site in terms of geographical position and altitude, the more important it becomes to have shelter and sunshine.

The best possible site would be one in the southern part of the country, less than 100 m (325 feet) above sea level, in an area of low rainfall; sheltered by the lie of the land from prevailing winds, yet not so enclosed that air cannot circulate between the vines; and on a south-facing slope which continues below the vineyard to allow frosts and mists to collect safely below the site. The soil should be light and well drained. A level site would be almost as good as a south slope, provided that it is really well drained and not in a frost pocket. Slopes facing south-west and south-east are also good for vines. At Lamber-hurst Priory it has been proved that grapes will ripen even on a north-east slope, facing away from the prevailing wind.

Anybody who is going to invest in a commercial vineyard would be extremely brave to start off without the perfect site. The Chilsdown Vineyard near Singleton in West Sussex would appear to be such a site, sloping gently south, with trees on the northern perimeter and hills round about, the soil a mixture of clay, silt, loam and chalk. In 1977, a difficult year because of the rain and the cool summer, Chilsdown produced 10 per cent of the total English wine output from only 1 per cent of the total area of English vineyards.

Mr and Mrs Barrett's vineyard at Felsted in Essex is well worked and successful but has certain, if minor, disadvantages. It is 67 m (220 feet) up and on clay, and Mrs Barrett told me that if they were starting again, they would make every effort to find a lower site with a lighter soil.

When considering a site as a possible vineyard, it is very helpful to have a record of the day-degrees on that particular spot.

Day-degrees measure the air temperature above 10 °C (50 °F)—the temperature below which vines will not grow. A suitable site should have 800 day-degrees centigrade in a good year.

To calculate the day-degrees between bud-burst and harvest (which is the relevant period) the maximum and minimum centigrade tem-peratures are recorded daily in a ventilated (Stevenson) screen 1.2 m (4 feet) above the ground. To arrive at a monthly average, the highest and the lowest temperatures recorded during that month are added together and divided by two. Then 10 °C is subtracted from this figure, and the result is multiplied by the number of days in the relevant month to give the monthly total of day-degrees. At harvest time, the monthly figures are all added together to give the total number of day-degrees for the growing period.

To take an example, in May 1977 the highest temperature recorded in our garden was 24 °C and the lowest was 2 °C.

$$24+2 = 26$$
$$26 \div 2 = 13$$
$$13 - 10 = 3$$

There are 31 days in May, so the final figure of 3 is multiplied by 31 to give the total day-degrees for the month: 93 day-degrees.

It would indeed be lucky if a record of day-degrees was available for a particular site for a long enough period to give a true picture of its local climate. The Meteorological Office, London Road, Bracknell, Berkshire, can supplement information by providing details of temperatures in the locality, but these, of course, give only a general idea of climate in the area.

If the aim is to have a vineyard just large enough to supply family and friends, then the investment is small and the grower can afford to take a few chances. If the vines do not crop as well as they would on an ideal site, this does not really matter. The home grower will simply allot the most suitable piece of ground which is available, plant the vines and hope for the best. Very often, in the more sheltered confines of a garden, and with the attention which can be given to vines grown on a small scale, they will crop better than vines in the average commercial vineyard.

CHAPTER FOUR

❧ *Preparing the Ground*

Vines in the Garden

Vines need well drained soil which is free from weeds and not too rich. If a few vines are to be planted here and there in a garden, then well drained places should be chosen and soggy, heavy positions avoided.

In well cultivated ground a hole dug 300 mm (1 foot) deep is quite adequate. Some compost and a handful of bonemeal should be mixed with the soil when planting the vine, and this will help to give it a good start.

In heavy soils or uncultivated ground the topsoil should be removed to one spit deep (the full length of a spade blade) and set aside separately from the topsoil. The bottom of the hole should then be broken up well with a spade. In heavy soils, throw into the bottom of the hole some freely draining material, such as broken crocks, bits of brick, stones, gravel or whatever is available. If using rubble, avoid fresh mortar which can harm the roots. Old mortar is fine. A little farmyard manure can then be put into the hole and covered with an upside-down turf, or with topsoil; add more topsoil and mix the top layer with a little damp peat or some well rotted compost. The roots can be spread out in this and then the subsoil mounded over to the desired level. If the subsoil is very clayey, however, it is better not to use it at all, but to replace it with topsoil.

Preparing a Vineyard

CLEARING THE WEEDS

When a vineyard is to be planted, whether of kitchen-garden size or large scale, the choice is either to pursue a scorched-earth policy, with not a vestige of weed or grass to be seen, or to plant in weed-free strips between grass lanes. If hand labour is being used, as it generally is in garden vineyards, it is much less effort to mow grass lanes than to keep the whole area weed-free. Some growers have found that grass in the lanes has led to potash deficiency, particularly on chalky soils, but many others are very happy with their grass.

Even in a mechanized vineyard there can be advantages to keeping grass lanes. On clay, for example, it is almost impossible to go on the land at all, even on foot, in wet weather if there is no grass to walk on, and in winter, jobs such as pruning would be a nightmare, slithering around in gumboots, while machinery could not possibly be used in wet conditions. Grass can also reduce soil erosion on hillsides where the soil is light and easily washed down. The main problem is that creeping weeds, particularly couch-grass, can invade the strips where the vines are growing.

Some growers compromise by applying a very diluted dose of herbicide to the grass lanes, which inhibits but does not extinguish grass growth. A quarter of the recommended quantity of herbicide should be tried initially.

It is desirable to have thoroughly clean ground before planting vines. Swiss research has shown that vines planted in clean soil establish a good root system far more quickly than vines which have competition from weeds and grasses. In infested ground it may take a full year or even two years to achieve a clean soil. A D A S (the Agricultural Development and Advisory Service of the Ministry of Agriculture, Fisheries and Food) recommends a combined fallow and herbicide method. One farmer in Kent grows corn for two years where the new vines are to go. The herbicides, which are cleared for use on corn, have cleaned the ground completely and he uses sprays to keep it that way. The first vines that he planted were not in clean ground and, despite many herbicide treatments, the weeds still persist. If a weed-free vineyard is desired, then it is very much easier to deal with the weeds before planting rather than plant in a hurry and rely on herbicides to deal with weed problems.

While it is desirable to plant vines in cleared, weed-free ground it is quite possible to treat them in a far more cavalier fashion. Mr Bernard Theobald of Westbury Farm in Berkshire has planted 15 acres of vines in grassland. He has simply treated strips of grass with Gramoxone, dug holes in the strips and planted the vines in a strip of black polythene 1 m wide, using more Gramoxone as necessary to keep the weeds down in the rows. This has indeed been our method in our own tiny vineyard, which is quite inaccessible to machinery. Mr Theobald's vines are growing vigorously. They fruit well and seem quite untroubled by their rough treatment at planting time. Mr Theobald would not claim that this method is ideal, but as a farmer who expects his vineyard to pay its way, he did not feel that the expense of thorough clearance of the ground could be justified.

Obviously, before clearing strips of ground for planting, the grower must have already decided exactly where the vines are to go and how far apart they are to be planted. This is discussed in Chapter 6.

DRAINAGE

Before planting vines, it is essential to check that the ground is properly drained. If planting on farm land, it is worth asking ADAS if it has any details of previous drainage schemes on the site. In some areas there are records going back to before the Second World War.

If the site is sloping and the soil is reasonably light, the natural drainage will probably be adequate. To check, dig holes or trenches about 1 m (3 feet) deep at various places over the site; if it is poorly drained, the water will stand in the holes for days after rain, only a few centimetres below the level of the surface of the soil. Such wet soil would rot the roots of the vines and eventually the plants would die. The most common cause of death in vines is asphyxiation of the roots caused by poor drainage.

Methods of improving drainage are:

Subsoiling is used on land which has been previously farmed, to break up the compacted layer of subsoil, known as a soil pan, which can occur where heavy machinery has been used. If done correctly, this helps considerably to drain the soil. It is done by agricultural contractors using heavy machinery and is therefore an expensive operation.

Open drainage ditches are quite effective but they need a lot of maintenance and clearing out every winter. They are normally dug along the boundaries of fields, by a hedge or fence, where they do not get in anybody's way. On sloping ground they are dug obliquely across the slope to intercept the water as it drains downhill and send it where it will do no harm.

Pipe drains are expensive but extremely efficient. They can be laid by hand – with a great deal of sweat. The clay or plastic pipes can be bought from builders' merchants. They are laid in trenches about 1 m

(3 feet) deep and covered with a layer of either straw or gravel. This is to prevent soil blocking the gaps between the pipes and thus making it impossible for the water to run into the pipes and be carried away. Finally, the soil is replaced and firmed down.

Mole drainage is very effective in clay soils, when combined with tile drains, but it may well have to be re-done from time to time, which can be tricky once the vines are planted. It is done by a mole plough, which draws a channel through the subsoil and at the same time cracks and disturbs the topsoil. The mole channels pass over the deeper tile drains and through the layer of permeable gravel or beach which covers the tiles. In suitable clay soil, the mole channels will stay open for five to ten years.

The Ministry of Agriculture has useful leaflets on mole drainage and other drainage systems. These can be obtained from Ministry of Agriculture, Fisheries and Food Publications, Tolcarne Drive, Pinner, Middlesex, HA5 2DT.

IMPROVING THE SOIL STRUCTURE

On heavy land, drainage can be much improved in time by adding humus in large quantities to the soil. At Horam, Mr Jack Ward of the Merrydown Wine Company planted eight hundred vines on a level site on heavy clay, which had once been used as a brick field. All the vines died. Nothing daunted, he tried again. Drainage ditches and a few tile drains were laid, but these, he found, made little appreciable difference on this very difficult site. Success came when compost, made from apple residue (a by-product of Merrydown Cider) mixed with straw and a small proportion of chicken litter, was applied in massive quantities. A layer of this compost 150 mm (6 inches) deep was put on the entire vineyard and was added to year by year, taking different parts of the vineyard in rotation. Now, after seven years, the soil is friable and in good heart.

Mr Ward was fortunate in having such vast quantities of compost available. Alternative sources of humus could be peat, although this is far too expensive to use for more than a few vines, or straw, which can be ploughed into the soil. Green manuring is much used on the Continent; for this, a crop, usually mustard, is allowed to grow high, then cut and left to wilt for a few days, after which it is ploughed into the soil. The best method in a vineyard is to plant alternate rows with the green manure crop; the clear rows are then used by workers and machinery. The next year, the process is reversed so that the rows previously clear are planted with the green manure crop, and it is the turn of the other rows to be left clear.

Whatever treatment is used, the aim is to lighten rather than enrich the soil. Too much nitrogenous manure, such as chicken litter and farmyard manure, would provide too rich a mixture for the vines, which would then produce leaf and cane rather than fruit, and the sappy growth would be vulnerable to fungal infections.

LIMING AND FERTILIZING

Soil for vines should have a pH of between 6 and 7, on the low side in light soils and on the high side in heavy soils. It should contain adequate quantities of nitrogen, potash and phosphates and contain minerals such as iron and manganese. If the pH is lower than 6, then the soil will be too acid to please the vines and lime should be added to redress the balance.

In limy and chalky soils the pH will naturally be high, and on very chalky soils only vines which are lime tolerant should be grown on their own roots. Most of the European vines like chalk. A lime-tolerant rootstock should be used for grafted vines. Humus, compost and manure improve chalky soils and so, in time, do acid-reacting fertilizers. These include ammonium sulphate, which is the most acidifying, and, to a lesser extent, ammonium nitrate and superphosphate, but the acidifying effect is extremely slow.

Nitrogen, potash and phosphates are contained in organic fertilizers such as farmyard manure and compost into which some animal matter, for example, chicken manure, has been incorporated. Alternatively, artificial fertilizers can be used. The time of preparation for planting is the last chance to dig fertilizers deep into the soil, where they will provide a store of food for the vines over a long period.

A soil analysis should be done before planting. If the soil analysis report reveals potash deficiency, a very heavy dressing of potash should be ploughed as deeply as possible into the soil. The Ministry of Agriculture recommends using 375 kg to 1 hectare ($2\frac{1}{4}$ acres) of potash for the purpose, compared to an annual application of 125 kg of potash which it recommends for normal soils. Local branches of the Agricultural Development and Advisory Service (ADAS) provide a soil-sampling service. Either ADAS will send someone to take samples, as many as are required, or the grower can take samples himself and send them in for analysis. Ideally, if the vineyard is to be of any size, samples should be taken from several places and these should be separately analysed, for soil can vary considerably over quite small distances. ADAS charges separately for each sample and at £6 per analysis this can become an expensive item. It is cheaper to take the samples oneself and send them in. The commercial grower would find detailed soil analysis well worth while; the rest of us will probably make do with a more perfunctory assessment of the soil's needs.

After taking the samples, ADAS reports back, giving details of soil content and recommendations for fertilizing and liming. This service is available to the amateur as well as the commercial grower. Commercial firms will also come to analyse soil and recommend treatments, but naturally their advice will not always be totally disinterested.

Vine-growing is so new and comparatively small scale in this country that unless an adviser is found, either at ADAS or at one of the commercial firms, who has interested himself in vines, it may well be that while the liming recommendations and such things as treatment for magnesium deficiency are most valuable, the general advice is not that helpful. ADAS is also extremely busy with more mainstream activities and is not encouraged to spend a great deal of time on vines. Even Bob Farrar, the head of the Viticulture Research Department at Wye College, funded partly by the Department of Hop Research at Wye and partly by the English Vineyards Association, is concerned chiefly with hops. In the same way, commercial suppliers, so helpful when consulted on one's potatoes or roses, are apt to be ignorant of the needs of vines.

So having established the pH of the soil and checked on its fertility, a certain amount of guesswork usually takes place. When preparing for planting, the rule of thumb is to lime if necessary, to redress any obvious deficiencies but to go easy on nitrogen.

Bulky organic fertilizers improve the texture and the general health and fertility of the soil and the time of preparation for planting is ideal for a generous application of compost or farmyard manure. Once planted and growing, the look of the vines will give a fairly good idea of whether they are getting the nourishment they need, and the professional grower will supplement his own observations with soil analysis, and perhaps leaf analysis as well. Many growers have a yearly analysis carried out, but every four to five years is recommended.

WINDBREAKS

If the vineyard is very exposed, some kind of windbreak will have to be provided. Belts of trees can be planted against the prevailing winds.

In one very windy vineyard, Lamberhurst Priory in Kent, there are windbreaks every fifteen rows; most people do not resort to such extreme measures. Suitable varieties of trees for windbreaks could be cricket-bat willow, poplar or Italian alder. These trees break the force of the wind but allow enough fresh air through to keep the vines healthy. Long Ashton Research Station near Bristol has done research on windbreaks and will provide expert advice.

Hideous-looking plastic windbreaks (Paraweb) are available and can be useful while natural windbreaks are growing. These are supplied by Fyffes Monro Horticultural Sundries Ltd, Forstal Road, Aylesford, Maidstone, Kent.

CHAPTER FIVE

✿ *Ordering the Vines*

What to buy and where to buy them

Several nurserymen now stock vines suitable for growing out of doors, and if you want only a few vines it may be convenient to buy them from a nursery. However, it is an expensive way to buy vines. Most vineyards now propagate and sell cuttings from their vines and some also import vines from the Continent to sell to the public. Lists of suppliers are given in Appendix 7.

Rootstocks

Arguments continue to rage in the vine world about whether, in Britain, vines should be planted on their own roots or grafted on to rootstocks. Grafted vines are considerably more expensive than vines on their own roots and they are also somewhat more difficult to establish because the graft is vulnerable to frosts and drying wind.

The advantages of using grafted vines are, first, that the choice of the correct rootstock can make an enormous difference to the performance of the vine and, second, that grafted vines are resistant to the insect pest phylloxera, which is endemic on the Continent but has so far not become established in the United Kingdom. To quote Tony Heath, Horticultural Advisory Officer of ADAS and a great vine enthusiast,

There may be no phylloxera in the British Isles at present but since 1863 there have been twenty recorded cases, ranging from Scotland, Ireland and Wales to the Home Counties and London. All prudent growers of vines should grow only rootstocks resistant to this pest. It is more than likely that phylloxera will be seen in the UK again and those who grow non-grafted vines do so at their peril.

The position was somewhat confused in late 1978 when the Ministry of Agriculture Plant Health Division planned to control any possible phylloxera outbreak by means of a policy of total eradication, of grafted

and non-grafted vines alike. However, ADAS would still recommend
planting grafted vines.

As far as choice of rootstock is concerned, expert advice should be
taken before planting a commercial vineyard. All should be resistant
to phylloxera; some are more vigorous than others; some tolerate
chalk or poor drainage.

The following are the most important in the United Kingdom:

5BB   Suits most conditions. Vigorous. Tolerates up to 20 per cent chalk
in soil.

125AA   Rather less vigorous than 5BB. Tolerates poor drainage.

5C   Less vigorous than either 5BB or 125AA; suitable for rich, deep
soils. Tolerates up to 40 per cent chalk.

S04   Tolerates probably up to 40 per cent chalk; tolerates rather poor
drainage.

41B   Suitable for very chalky soils (up to 60 per cent); not vigorous.

If vines are to be planted on difficult soils, such as very chalky soils or
heavy clay, then there is a strong case for planting only grafted vines
on rootstocks adapted to these special conditions.

On the other hand, the cost of grafted vines, when compared with
that of expanding a vineyard with home-grown cuttings reared at
practically no expense, is a major item. On the Continent growers have
a huge capital nest-egg, left by preceding generations, of established
vineyards, buildings, equipment, expertise, skilled labour and proven
methods. In Britain this capital is now being invested over a few years:
workers are being trained, buildings erected, vine varieties and cultivation methods are being tested. This is a major factor in the rather
high prices now being charged for English wines. So vine-growers save
money where they can and rearing cuttings for further planting is one
of the obvious ways to economize.

One grower, Mrs Pamela Smith of Flexerne Vineyard, East Sussex,
has gone to the extreme of planting an entire 2½-acre vineyard with the
progeny of a bundle of Müller-Thurgau cuttings. As she points out, the
saving on a 5-acre vineyard through planting home-grown vines, rather
than buying in grafted vines, can be in excess of £5000 and this sum
would be enough to purchase the land.

It is vitally important that the vines should be free of virus diseases
(thought by some plant pathologists to be more of a long-term threat
to vines in the United Kingdom than phylloxera) and free of any other
infections. One of the major advantages of buying grafted stock from

Germany, for example, is that an enormous amount of research and effort has gone into producing vines with a clean bill of health. When buying rooted cuttings in Britain, the buyer can only form his own opinion of the vigour and health of the parent vines and of the cuttings.

Choosing varieties

There are so many varieties of vines now being grown in the British Isles that the choice can be bewildering. The Continental research stations have come up with dozens of new varieties, but information on how they perform in Britain is hard to come by. To make the choice even more difficult, the same variety will give very different results not only in different vineyards but also when grafted on to different rootstocks.

Any new grower would be well advised to find out what varieties are being grown successfully in vineyards similar in soil and position to his own. These vineyards should be visited; the wine should be tasted and methods studied. Vine-growers are extremely helpful and generous with advice to newcomers, but it would be tactful to visit vineyards, initially at any rate, as a paying member of the public. Most of the larger vineyards have open days or regular tours. If not, it is nearly always possible to write or telephone and arrange a visit. A list of vineyards open to the public is given in Appendix 5.

The more vineyards that can be visited and the more wines that can be tasted, the better. The quality of wines varies widely and, while many English vineyards produce very good wines, there is unfortunately some poor English wine being made. Whether the grower is merely making enough wine for himself, his family and friends, or intending to make wine to sell commercially, the quality should be all important. If English wine is to succeed in wine-flooded Europe, then it must be of the finest quality. And if the home-grower is going to the trouble of making his own wine, the last thing he wants is a cellar full of plonk.

Many of the most promising varieties of vines are hybrids, that is they are bred by crossing a European vine with an American variety. These vines are frowned upon by the EEC, and it is quite possible that, as the area planted with vines in the United Kingdom increases, the EEC may impose the restrictions on planting which are already in force on the Continent. This would affect commercial growers only; amateurs are free to grow what varieties they wish. Grapes from hybrid vines are not allowed to be used in the making of 'quality wines'.

There are enormous vested interests discouraging hybrid vines. Hybrids are often very prolific, which is serious in the EEC with its rapidly rising wine lake. The pesticide manufacturers dislike the hybrids' greater resistance to disease. Suppliers of grafted vines are worried by the hybrids' resistance to phylloxera, which would remove the chief incentive to the planting of vines on rootstocks, and could eventually mean the loss of many jobs.

EEC regulations divide varieties of vines into three categories: those that are *recommended* for growing in the United Kingdom and are the only vines that can be used for 'quality wines'; those that are *authorized*; and the remainder, which are considered *experimental*. The British are lucky in that the UK is the only member state to be allowed to plant all sorts of varieties of vines and make wines from them on an experimental basis. In some cases the *recommended* varieties appear to be so unsuitable for the British climate that I have wondered about the motives of the EEC regulation makers. However, as knowledge of the EEC guidelines is essential for commercial growers they are included in the following descriptions of varieties.

The following list describes a large number of varieties which are being grown in the British Isles today with varying degrees of success, giving such information as I have been able to obtain. Members of the English Vineyards Association have been particularly helpful in letting me know what results they have had from the vines that they grow. However, as one grower said, 'Ask me again in ten years' time.' English viticulture has not been established long enough for any clear conclusions to be drawn and it still remains to be seen which will be the best vines for the United Kingdom.

If more than one variety is to be planted, then they should either ripen at more or less the same time, so that a blended wine can be made, or a sufficient quantity of each variety should be planted to make it worth while fermenting the different wines separately. It must also be remembered that spraying becomes more complicated when more than one variety is planted if the flowering and ripening dates do not coincide (see Chapter 8).

Black varieties are usually planted only for their (white) juice, because so far no good red wine has been made commercially in Britain (but see the Zweigeltrebe entry on page 30).

Having decided what vines should be grown, they should be ordered as far in advance as possible and certainly by October if the vines are to be planted the following spring.

The varieties which are *recommended* and *authorized* by the EEC for growth in the United Kingdom may well be less suited to our conditions than others which so far are *experimental*.

'Early ripeners' are those which ripen before the end of September; 'mid-season' ripen in October and 'late' ripen in November or December – or not at all. These dates apply to warmer areas; growers at high altitudes or in cooler parts of the country may find the 'early' varieties are the only ones to ripen regularly in the open.

Descriptions of varieties

Albalonga. A new variety with a rather high acidity but giving quite good yields of white grapes. Ripens mid-season.

Auxerrois. Although 'recommended' by the EEC this variety needs a very good year to make a good wine: resistant to botrytis and oidium and can tolerate poor drainage better than some vines.

Bacchus. There are good reports of this new vine. It is a prolific cropper, the grapes are high in sugar and it ripens wood well; the fruit ripens in October. It is 'authorized' by the EEC.

Baco 1. A very vigorous French hybrid which will grow quickly over a garage or shed. The black grapes give a harsh, thin wine. It likes chalk.

Black Hamburg (Trollinger). This variety will not ripen in the UK, except in a glasshouse.

Blue Portuguese. This variety gives enormous quantities of inferior black grapes; it is very prone to disease.

Brant. An ornamental Canadian vine, immensely vigorous and very prolific, bearing small, sweet, black grapes which make an undistinguished wine. Resistant to mildew.

Chambourcin. A French hybrid. The black grapes ripen early and it is said to crop well but little information has come in as yet.

Chardonnay (Pinot Blanc). A French variety. This is the Chablis vine. It bears small bunches of grapes which make a high-quality wine. Unfortunately it is choosy and needs a very favourable site to crop well. It ripens late. Reports on its performance vary. Mr Graham Barrett at Felsted, Essex, says it is his vineyard's best vine for quality. The Paget brothers at Chilsdown planted five thousand of this vine but many failed to establish themselves and yields have been very low. They might well have succeeded on a more vigorous rootstock, eg., So4 or 5BB.

Chasselas (Gutedel). There are both red and white varieties of this vine, which is rather late to ripen and suitable for greenhouses, but can be grown in the open in favourable sites, perhaps against a wall. It is used for eating as well as wine-making. It is rather subject to botrytis.

Ehrenfelser. A high-quality, Riesling-type vine which is, however, rather late ripening in the open in Britain except on good sites. It has done better than some at Wye during the cool summers of 1977 and 1978. It is 'authorized' by the EEC.

Faber. A mid-season ripener, giving a good yield of high-quality grapes. It is a new variety and there is not enough information on its performance in Britain as yet, but it sounds promising. It is 'authorized' by the EEC.

Gargarin Blue. A Russian hybrid, bearing early-ripening black grapes. Good reports on it have come in from two gardeners who have tried it out on a small scale, one in Wiltshire and one near Bristol.

Gamay Noir. A Beaujolais vine. Mr Baillie Grohman of Hascombe Vineyard in Surrey has planted some vines for experiment which are doing quite well so far.

Gutenborner. A late-ish ripening, new variety. The white grapes are of good quality but the vines are subject to disease, especially botrytis. It is said to do well when grown high on the Geneva Double Curtain system.

Huxelrebe. A German vine developed in the late 60s. The large green grapes have a muscat flavour not liked by everybody. One grower told me: 'It tastes like wet dog fur.' It dislikes chalk, tends to overcrop and is prone to botrytis. Other growers, notably Mr S. W. Greenwood of New Hall Vineyard and the Merrydown Wine Company at Horam Manor in East Sussex, speak highly of it. Ripens in October. It is 'authorized' by the EEC.

Kanzler. A new variety, ripens mid-season, high in quality but low in yield and subject to diseases. 'Authorized' by the EEC.

Kerner. Another new variety, giving high-quality Riesling-type grapes but ripens rather late for Britain. 'Authorized' by the EEC.

Madeleine Angevine. Reliable, good cropper, giving good-quality white grapes. Sometimes the wine has a pronounced muscat taste. Very early ripening which is unsatisfactory in warmer areas, as wasps attack the fruit. Mr D. S. Bates has found it does well in Leicestershire; Mr Don of Elmham Vineyard in Norfolk says that it is one of his two most successful varieties. 'Authorized' by the EEC.

Madeleine Royale. This vine is also 'authorized' by the EEC but I have not heard from anyone who is growing it.

Madeleine Sylvaner. Very early ripening and therefore prone to damage from wasps and flies. 'A poor cropper and indifferent wine,' was the comment of Mr Kelly of An Foras Talúntais (the Irish Agricultural Institute) in Co Waterford, Republic of Ireland. Other growers find it crops well. Another EEC 'authorized' variety.

Mariensteiner. A new variety, good quality and rather high acidity. It is grown by the Merrydown Wine Company at its Kingston Vineyard but is not so successful as the company's other varieties. 'Authorized' by the EEC.

Morio-Muskat. This new variety needs a very warm position to do well and is not recommended for open vineyards. It crops heavily and the wine has a strong bouquet. It is subject to disease.

Müller-Thurgau (Riesling Sylvaner). The most popular grape with growers in Britain, but it does need two good years in succession to ripen wood and produce good crops. Acidity rather high, medium sugar content, it gives good wine where the soil suits it. However, it is not suited to all soils and the wine from some vineyards has an unpleasant taste. The vines should be planted at least 1.37 m (4½ feet) apart in rows 1.8 m (6 feet) apart to stimulate movement of fresh air or botrytis will be encouraged. Summer pruning recommended. Ripens in October. It is subject to disease, especially botrytis and sometimes dead arm. 'Recommended' by the EEC. The wine should be drunk young after perhaps nine to twelve months and should not be kept longer than two years.

Muscat Hamburg. Best grown under glass but can ripen on a warm wall. The black, muscat-flavoured grapes are used for dessert, not for wine.

Muscat de Saumur. A white, muscat, dessert grape.

Noblessa. Early ripening, new variety. High in sugar but a poor cropper and subject to botrytis.

Nobling. Mid-season ripening, new variety. The wine is fruity but the vine is subject to diseases.

Optima. Mid-season ripening, another new variety. Sugar and acid content good and the wood ripens well. Subject to botrytis.

Ortega. A new variety, said to be 'the best of the earlies' but, of course, liable to be attacked by wasps. Not particularly vigorous. Should not be picked too late or it can lose too much acidity. Wine matures rather slowly and should perhaps be kept three or four years, or even longer. 'Authorized' by the EEC.

Perle de Czaba. An early ripening, white grape. Grown in Eastern Europe; likes a fairly rich soil. Not very prolific.

Pinot Blanc. See Chardonnay.

Pinot Gris (Ruländer). Needs a favourable site. Light cropper. It seems to like the heavier soils, but a small-scale grower at 122 m (400 feet) on limestone in Gloucestershire reports that it 'gives a superb wine in a good year'. 'Authorized' by the EEC.

Pinot Meunier (Müllerrebe). Disease resistant and gives a moderately good wine. A champagne grape, it is suitable for making sparkling white wines should you be so inclined. Wrotham Pinot or Dusty Miller is a variety of this grape which has probably been grown in Britain for centuries, but nevertheless ripens too late to be suitable for any but the most favourable sites. Pinot Meunier is 'recommended' by the EEC.

Pinot Noir (Spätburgunder). Top in quality but poor in quantity. A champagne grape also much grown in Burgundy. Mr S. W. Greenwood, of New Hall Vineyard in Essex, says that this is his most successful variety, 'not cropping heavily but producing a wine of outstanding quality'. Mr Reresby Sitwell, who has a vineyard at Renishaw in Derbyshire, likes it too. Grown in the open it does well under cloches or on a south-facing wall. However, it does well at Wye in the open, even in poor years. It is 'authorized' by the EEC.

Pirovano. 14. A black, dessert grape which can give a good yield in a very good year. Not suitable for an open vineyard.

Précoce de Malingre. An early ripening, white grape, suitable for dessert as well as wine. Mr B. R. Grose grows it in his allotment at Beckenham in Kent and says that it is the best, most successful of the varieties he has there and that it crops heavily. However, Mr Graham Barrett of Felsted in Essex has found it to be a very poor cropper.

Rabaner. A new variety yielding white grapes of a Riesling type. It seems to like the heavier soils. Ripens mid-season. Mr Baillie Grohman has some of these vines at Hascombe Vineyard, Surrey.

Ramdas. A new hybrid bearing white grapes on attractive red canes. It is one of the varieties being tested at Wye College.

Regner. A new variety, rather like Müller-Thurgau, but some say the flavour is superior. The dense bunches are easy to harvest. It is resistant to botrytis but rather subject to oidium. Mid-season. Has done very well in tests at Wye College, being the most promising of their varieties and has done better than most in the cool summers of 1977 and 1978.

Reichensteiner. This is becoming very popular. It crops well, is fairly resistant to botrytis and its white grapes ripen mid-season. Makes delicately flavoured wine and the grapes have a high sugar content. Should not be picked too late or the acidity may be too low to give a good wine.

Riesling. A very high quality grape which, alas, ripens rather too late for Britain. Worth trying against a wall or in a very sheltered position. Fairly resistant to disease. The wine needs a year to mature.

Scheurebe. Low in yield, very late to ripen but very high quality. Mr Michael Waterfield has some Scheurebe vines at his vineyard, Marriage Hill, near Wye, Kent; he blends the juice with juice from Müller-Thurgau and Reichensteiner and says that it is the Scheurebe that gives his wine quality and flavour. It is also highly recommended by the Barretts of Felsted in Essex. Needs a sheltered site.

Schönburger (Rosa Muskat). Another high-quality grape, dicey in unpropitious weather but will make a delicious wine in good years. High in sugar; healthy growth. Major Colin Gillespie of Wootton Vineyards won first prize at Trier with his Schönburger '76.

Seibel 13053. Heavy cropping decorative vine (up to 9 kg/20 lb per vine). The black grapes make a red or rosé wine of variable quality. A report from the Long Ashton Research Station suggests that 'The strong flavour can be reduced by harvesting at maximum ripeness only and by fermenting on the skins for not more than twenty-four hours.' Grown commercially by Mr L. T. Bates of Kentish Vineyards, Mr John Astor of Kirby, Berkshire, and Mr Bernard Theobald of Westbury Farm, Berkshire, all of whom like it. Yet I have heard from many that the taste of the wine can be disagreeable. Obviously, wine from these grapes is tricky to make well. Resistant to mildew and can tolerate poor drainage.

Septimer. A new variety, high in sugar; fairly early to ripen; white grapes.

Seyval Blanc (Seyve-Villard 5/276). Very popular with growers for its hybrid vigour, resistance to disease and heavy crops of white grapes. It is happy on chalk and responds well to spur pruning. Mr J. T. Edgerley finds that it does not like the soil (clay/loam) at his vineyard at Kelsale, Suffolk, and he has lost many of his vines. The wine is rather dull on its own but is used for blending with more distinguished varieties. 'Authorized' by the EEC.

Siegerrebe. Very early ripening and therefore vulnerable to damage from wasps and flies. The golden-brown grapes, with their muscat flavour, make good eating as well as delicious wine. Yields are poor. 'Authorized' by the EEC. Should not be harvested too late or too much acidity will be lost and the wine will be dull.

Sylvaner. Quite a good cropper but rather too late ripening for Britain and not very interesting in flavour.

Traminer. Fine-quality grapes but growth is weak and yields are low.

Wrotham Pinot (Dusty Miller). See Pinot Meunier.

Wurzer. A new variety, said to yield good crops of white grapes, high in sugar, which make a wine with a pleasant bouquet, but there is little information on its performance in Britain so far.

Zweigeltrebe. Another new variety, giving black grapes. It is now being tried at Wye College and is so far one of their most successful varieties. A red wine called Malteser, made from this grape in Austria, is available for sampling from the Merrydown Wine Company, who some years ago imported another Austrian red wine made from the Zweigelt grape, called Alter Knabe. Red wine, said to be 'acceptable' has been made at Long Ashton Research Station from Zweigeltrebe grapes.

CHAPTER SIX

❧ *Planting*

The first knotty problem, and it really is knotty, is how far apart to plant the vines. The Continental vine-growers have planted their vines closer and closer together as the vineyards have spread north. So the first English growers in the 1950s and 1960s tended to plant their vines closer together than would be recommended today. Mr Nigel Godden of Pilton Manor, Somerset, planted his 1.2 m (4 feet) apart with 1.2 m (4 feet) between the rows; Sir Guy Salisbury-Jones, who was the first in England to establish a twentieth-century commercial vineyard, initially planted his vines 0.9 m (3 feet) apart with 1.2 m (4 feet) between the rows.

It was soon realized that this close planting was only successful where there were troops of peasants rather than tractors providing the labour. It was also realized that, in a humid climate, close planting leads to a muggy atmosphere with its attendant evil of the curse of British vineyards – botrytis – and a diminution of the amount of sunlight available to each plant.

Some growers have followed these ideas to what they consider the logical conclusion, that is the Geneva Double Curtain; a system which has nothing to do with Switzerland but Geneva, New York, where the vines are planted very far apart with up to 3.7 m (12 feet) between the rows. The vines are then allowed to grow to a large size. The stem is allowed to grow up to a wire 1.5–1.8 m (5–6 feet) above the ground. Two permanent arms are then grown along the wire and the fruit is borne on canes from the spurs. These canes hang down on either side of the trellis in summer like two green curtains, hence the name, Geneva Double Curtain (GDC). This system is most persuasively advocated by Mr Theobald of Westbury Farm and anyone who is considering planting vines should certainly go to see his vineyard.

The advantage of the Geneva Double Curtain system is that, with only 400 vines planted to the acre there is a large saving in the cost of setting up the vineyard in vines, wires and labour. The advocates of the GDC are convinced that with the vines being allowed to grow to a considerable size, the crop per acre will be as high as, if not higher than, that obtained from the traditional systems. They are also confident that, in spite of the time taken for the vines to grow to such a size, a vineyard planted in this way will come into production just as soon as any other new vineyard. They point to the fact that a vine allowed to grow to a large size has a greatly increased leaf area and is thus able to make the very best use of the somewhat meagre British sunshine to produce larger crops of sweeter grapes. Finally, the Geneva Double Curtain system is highly suitable for mechanical harvesting once the vineyard is large enough to justify the expense of the machine. Mr Theobald intends to extend his vineyard to 50 acres and then, he feels, mechanical harvesting will be viable on his farm. Meanwhile, as he points out, hand picking and other work in his vineyard are far less effort with the grapes growing at a comfortable height above the ground, which is something that less agile growers might find interesting. At present he has 15 acres planted; the vines are vigorous and cropped well in the difficult, cool summer of 1978.

Most growers have so far remained unconvinced by Mr Theobald and stick to the Double Guyot system. In this the vines are planted comparatively close together, cut down each winter to leave two canes to bear fruit and a spur with two buds to provide replacement canes. The canes are tied down to a bottom wire about 450 mm (18 inches) above the ground. The flowers and later the grapes are carried on lateral shoots springing up from the tied-down canes, so more wires are necessary to support and control these laterals as they grow. A common arrangement is to have four double wires above the cane-bearing wires; the shoots are then tucked in between the double wires as they grow, which saves the work of tying in.

All this means a large investment in vines, wires and work compared to the Geneva Double Curtain, but most growers feel that a more intensive system will pay dividends in heavier crops and feel also that they will have their vines in full production earlier with the Guyot method. The spacing of the vines under the Guyot system can be as close as 0.9 m (3 feet) between the vines and 1.2 m (4 feet) between the rows, but as the vines grow this begins to feel very cramped and leaves little room for spraying and pruning. Growers who use machinery plant their rows from 1.8 to 2.7 m (6 to 9 feet) apart, depending on the size of their machines. Even if machines are not being used, it has been found that close planting is not a good idea in our humid climate. Müller-Thurgau is the vine most commonly grown in Britain and it is particularly vulnerable to botrytis. For this vine the *minimum* spacing distance recommended is 1.37 m (4½ feet) between the vines with 1.8 m (6 feet) between the rows. Wide spacing is also advisable when planting other vines subject to botrytis.

Guyot is by far the most popular system in British vineyards but Geneva Double Curtain has much to recommend it. If it can be proved to crop as well as Guyot, I feel that it will spread rapidly. These and other pruning systems are illustrated and discussed in more detail in Chapter 7.

Having decided on the spacing, it is easy to calculate the number of vines required, that is for those who are mathematically inclined. I find that I have to measure out the rows and then walk up and down, counting. Geneva Double Curtain uses 400 vines per acre; for the various Guyot systems anything between 1,000 and 3,600 vines per acre are needed.

A support will be needed for each vine. Bamboo canes are most frequently used but some growers prefer to use something stronger, such as a metal support or a wooden stake. Wooden stakes last much longer than bamboos; metal stakes last indefinitely. Both are stronger than bamboos and give a better support to the vines, which can then be tied in more firmly and can grow straight up without any of those wiggles which tend to catch on machinery. However, bamboos are cheaper to buy and it is also quite easy to grow replacements in the garden. Wooden stakes can be acquired from local suppliers. Lamberhurst Priory Vineyard will supply suitable metal supports.

Soft plastic ties, which can be bought from farm suppliers, are useful for tying the young vines to their supports, for they do not chafe the vines and will stretch as the stems thicken.

Marking out the planting positions has to be done with great accuracy. If the vines are out of position they will get in the way of machines and will also be putting too much weight on the trellis of posts and wires, when this is finally erected, instead of growing up straight and firm. A rigid measure, such as a measuring stick or a steel tape, should be used. If the outside stakes are set in first, then it is easy to align the stakes within the rows by sighting along the lines.

Rows are conventionally planted to run north and south, but if planting on a slope, it is preferable to align them to run up and down the hill, for even quite small machines tend to slip sideways if used across a slope. Even if machines do not slip, they tend to dig in their lower wheels and heap up the soil in an undesirable manner. However, if the slope is very steep and soil erosion is a threat, it is sometimes better to plant the rows obliquely on the hillside, for erosion can be serious.

Rabbits can be a major nuisance: they adore nibbling young vines. A rabbit-proof fence with rabbit-proof gates around the perimeter of the vineyard gives peace of mind. A tip from one grower was, 'Don't forget to shut the gate; the rabbits will be in as soon as you turn your back.' Another grower was plagued with an enormous hare, with an equally enormous appetite, which wreaked much havoc until a neighbour managed to shoot it. It is possible to put a roll of wire around each vine and thus save the expense of the rabbit-proof fence, but this makes it more difficult to weed and look after the vines. This is, however, very much worth considering with low-density vines trained as in Geneva Double Curtain, for it is very much cheaper than wiring the perimeter of the vineyard. One grower optimistically relied on painting the young vines with Stockholm tar, but within two or three weeks the rabbits overcame their dislike of this and many vines were lost or damaged. Rabbits do not usually harm mature vines.

The vines should be planted while they are dormant, any time before May. However, this is not always possible. Luckily, vines are very resilient and they have been planted successfully in all sorts of conditions, in July, in September, in February, in drought and in drizzle. The best time to plant is in warm spring weather and April is the ideal month. If it is possible to run a hosepipe to the vineyard to water the vines well in and to give them a good drenching at intervals, should there be one of those desiccating spring droughts, so much the better. If the vines are planted in autumn they will be particularly vulnerable to waterlogging and good drainage will help.

When the vines arrive they should be unpacked immediately, washed thoroughly and checked to see that they are in good condition. The labels should be checked to make sure that the right varieties have been sent. The vines should have two or three good roots and plenty of finer rootlets. The wood should be green when cut. The graft (which can easily be recognized by the beginner by its calloused, knobbly look) should be firm.

If the vines cannot be planted out immediately, they are heeled into a moist shady place with their grafts completely covered by the soil.

Before planting, the roots of the vines are trimmed, 'like a toothbrush' said one grower, to about 75 mm (3 inches) in length. To prevent the roots drying out during planting, the vines can be stood in buckets of water. The shoot is cut back to two or three buds. Any roots growing from the side are removed.

A doctor, who has planted a small vineyard in Kent, had a sad experience with his first planting. He forgot that the earth would settle and sink in the holes and he ended up with each vine in a depression which in wet weather became a puddle. If the vines are planted in little mounds, these soon settle to the right level. The graft joint should be above soil level but then, as a temporary measure to protect the graft from frost and wind, the soil should be heaped up over the grafts until the warmer weather comes and the vines begin to grow, when it is raked back to leave the graft 50–75 mm (2–3 inches) above the soil.

Most people do not like using weedkillers near young vines, although some do use such poisons as Gramoxone (paraquat). To keep the weeds down, a hoe can be used. Mr Ian Paget estimated that he used to have 37 miles of hoeing to get through at Chilsdown. Black polythene strips are most efficient at suppressing weeds. I notice that those who have once used this method keep on using it for further plantings. The strips are laid along the rows and the vines planted in slits in the polythene.

Mr Bernard Theobald claims that his vines crop a year earlier if planted in black polythene because the soil warms up so well and this stimulates growth. Finally, the polythene does much to protect the young vines from drying out in hot weather.

At the Lamberhurst Priory Vineyards in Kent, they have an ingenious system of planting in polythene. After the soil has been manured, ploughed and levelled, a converted horticultural machine makes a furrow and lays the polythene in one operation; the vines are then planted in slits in the polythene. Weeds tend to grow where the soil overlaps the edges of the polythene to weight it down, but it is a comparatively simple matter to spray the weeds on these edges without affecting the vines. The polythene should survive for two or three years, after which it is possible to use sprays to keep weeds away from the rows.

When first planted, a vineyard is rather a pathetic sight: rows of little brown sticks and bamboo canes in bare earth or clinical plastic. But, once the vines begin to grow, their progress is amazingly fast. A young vine can grow as much as 1.8 m (6 feet) in a season and by September the vineyard will look encouragingly different.

Take a note, before the leaves fall, of any vine which has failed to survive. Once the leaves have gone it is difficult to remember which vines are dead and will need to be replaced, and replacement should be done before bud-burst in spring.

CHAPTER SEVEN

❧ *Pruning and Training*

The principles of pruning a vine are very simple. The aim is to channel energy into the production of as much good-quality fruit as possible by cutting away superfluous growth and letting in light and air to a balanced, healthy plant.

For the first two years, top growth is kept very restricted while the vine forms a vigorous root system and the permanent wood of the stem (and the branches, if there are to be branches) that will last throughout its life. No vine should be allowed to fruit for the first two years after planting.

The mature vine is pruned each winter to provide fresh fruit-bearing shoots and trained so that each leaf is exposed to as much sun and air as possible.

There are two basic ways to prune. One is to grow long canes each year from the top of the stem of the vine. The other is to have a vine

Spur pruning a vine which has been trained against a wall

with permanent branches which are spur pruned each year, rather like an espaliered fruit tree. This second method is the one generally used for vines grown on walls or in greenhouses; it is also used in open vineyards for the Geneva Double Curtain system (see pages 31–2 and pages 53–5). The first method is, however, by far the most common in open vineyards and the system used is almost invariably Guyot.

Pruning is done in winter while the vine is dormant. December and January are the best months, but often the grower gets behind with the job and there is many a vineyard where pruning is still going on in April. If pruning is done when the sap is rising then the vine, notoriously, 'bleeds'. One cane can lose $4\frac{1}{2}$ litres (1 gallon) of sap and if the tip of the cane is cut daily then between 23 and 32 litres (5 and 6 gallons) of liquid can be collected. This sounds appalling but, according to researchers, it does not harm the vine.

Summer pruning after the first two years consists only of trimming shoots when they grow too long in the late summer, and rubbing off unwanted buds from the vine's stem. Some people also remove a few leaves from below and around the bunches of grapes to let in a healthy blast of fresh air to discourage mildews. The chief systems are described below in detail.

Double Guyot system

YEAR ONE

The newly planted vine will have been pruned to two buds at planting time.

May. The shoots will probably begin to grow. Some vines may well take longer and they should not be written off for a while; the shock of replanting may delay them by several weeks. Cold weather can also delay growth.

When the shoots are 25–50 mm (1–2 inches) long, the strongest shoot is chosen and all the others are removed. Only one shoot is allowed to grow in the first year.

This one shoot is tied to the stake every 150 mm (6 inches) or so as it grows.

June to August. Pinch out all lateral shoots as they grow, leaving one leaf.

Late September. Pinch out the leading shoot.

Winter. Prune the shoot right back to two or three buds.

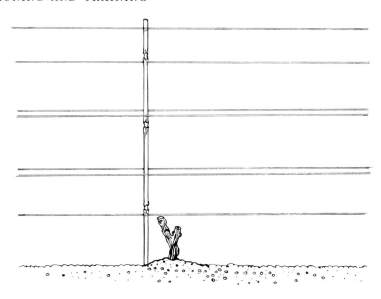

Double Guyot: a newly planted vine which has been pruned to two buds

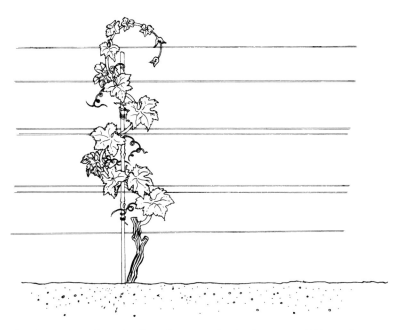

Double Guyot: one shoot is allowed to grow in the first year. All laterals are pinched out

Close-up of a lateral shoot, growing in the angle between the leaf and the stem. The bud beside the shoot should not be damaged when pinching out the shoot

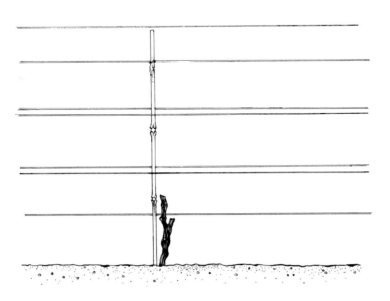

Double Guyot: the first summer's growth is cut back to two buds at pruning time

The first winter after planting, while the ground is soft, is a good time to put up the trellis of posts and wires, because in the following summer the vines, growing vigorously, will tug at their supports in a strong wind and may snap bamboo canes at ground level.

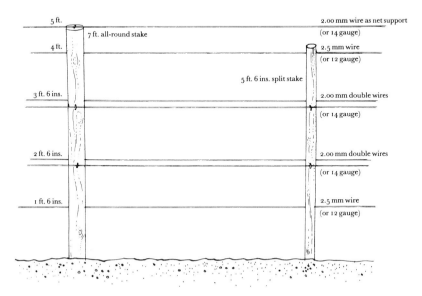

A trellis for vines. Heights above the ground can be altered to suit the grower. This particular system can be seen at Flexerne Vineyard, East Sussex

The end posts in the rows need extra support to take the strain. Some growers anchor the end posts with wire guy ropes attached to anchor disks set outside the rows and many is the time that I have tripped over one of these.

A better arrangement is to use a wooden support stake or wires and to strengthen the straining post further by an overhead wooden crossbar nailed firmly to the next stake, which should be one of the sturdy 2.12 m (7 ft) posts. In this way the space at the end of the rows can be used to accommodate one more vine and there is no risk of breaking your neck falling over an anchor wire.

Chestnut is the longest lasting wood for the posts, which should be ordered pointed, peeled and dipped. Larch is another possibility. Creosote should not be used to preserve the wood; posts that have been tarred or softwood posts treated with a preservative such as Tanalith are best. Farms and estates can usually cut and use their own posts.

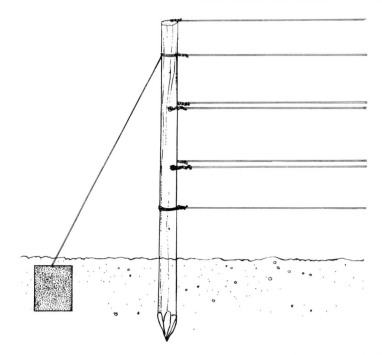

Post and wire trellis: the end post is strengthened by a straining wire attached to an anchor disc

Plastic wire (Thor Monofil) is available from Fyffes Monro of Maidstone, but it is not recommended for vines by most of those who have tried it; it is fatally easy to cut these wires when harvesting or pruning. Metal wires should be 12 gauge and 14 gauge. A wire strainer should be used if the rows are to be at all long (see drawing). A post-hole borer can be hired or borrowed for putting in the posts. A sledge-hammer tends to split the wood; an admirable tool is the 'Drivall', which looks like an enormous heavy metal jug with two handles. The Drivall is put over the top of the stake, lifted up and thumped down until the stake is firmly in the ground. The vine supports are tied to the trellis.

YEAR TWO

The programme for the second year is very similar to that followed in the first. In May, when the shoots begin to grow, the strongest is selected to grow and all other shoots are removed. As the shoot grows upwards, it is tied to the supporting cane. All the laterals are removed

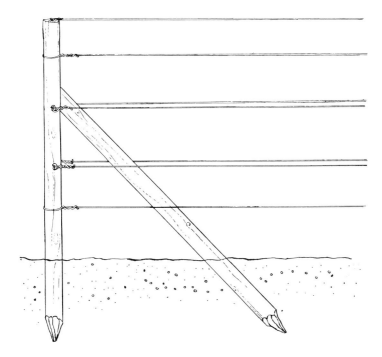

Post and wire trellis: the end post is supported by a cross member stake

as they appear, leaving one leaf. If any fruit appears it should be removed so that the vine can concentrate on making good growth of cane and roots. The leading shoot is pinched out in late September.

In winter the cane is cut back from bud to bud until ripened wood is reached. This can be recognized by its pale green inside and brown woody outside. If, at this stage, the remaining cane is very short, or thin and weakly, then it is cut right back to two buds, thus postponing fruiting for one more year, while the vine establishes itself. It will catch up with the other vines later and nothing will be gained by impatience at this stage in its life. Vines which are not ready to crop are treated in the third year as if they were in their second year.

If the ripened wood is 'pencil thick' and of a reasonable length, then preparations for next year's harvest can proceed. All buds on the cane up to the level of the bottom wire are rubbed off – for below this level the cane becomes the permanent stem of the plant.

The remaining length of cane is pruned to ten buds, bent gently down to the bottom wire and tied. The canes can be stiff; in damp weather they are considerably more flexible, so a damp spell is a good

time to do the job. The canes bend more easily once the sap begins to
rise, so if difficulty is experienced the job may be left until March or
April.

YEAR THREE

This is the year of the first harvest, so from now on the laterals are not
removed, as they were in the first two years, because it is the laterals
that will bear the fruit.

May. Rub out any buds that appear below the bottom wire. All other
buds and laterals are left to grow on. The laterals will begin to shoot
upwards at an amazing rate. As they grow, they are tucked in between
the double wires.

July. The flowers usually appear in early July but sometimes in late
June. After flowering there may be a set of fruit which is somewhat too
heavy for immature vines. Half, or even more, of the bunches should
probably be removed in this, the first year of cropping, but this very
much depends on the vigour and strength of the vines.

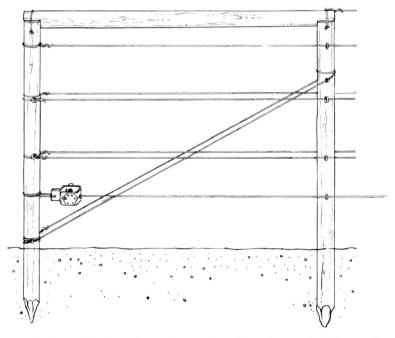

Post and wire trellis: the end post is strengthened by wires strained diagonally
from the second post and by a half-round wooden cross bar, nailed over the top

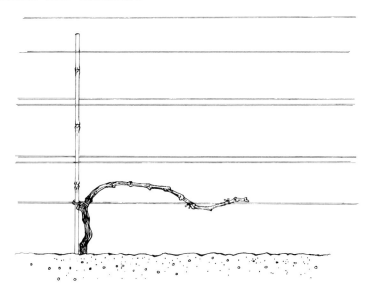

Double Guyot: in its second season, the vine is treated as in its first season, until pruning time, when the single cane is tied down for fruiting in the following year

August. When the laterals reach the top wire they are trimmed off at this level. In addition, many growers remove a few leaves below and around the bunches. Generally speaking, no other leaves should be removed; for the leaves are the sugar factories for the fruit, but if botrytis is a problem, it is a good thing to have fresh air moving around the bunches and in this case it is probably on balance better to pull off just these few leaves.

Early September. Put up some sort of protection from birds (see page 64).

Late September to October. Harvest the grapes.

Winter. All the year's growth is pruned away except for three strong canes which should be springing from as near the stem as possible.

Two of these canes are pruned to about 600 mm (2 feet) in length. These are gently bent down on either side of the vine and tied to the bottom wire.

The remaining cane is spur pruned to two buds. These will provide replacement canes for the following year.

PRUNING MATURE VINES

During the fourth and subsequent years, pruning and care continue as for year three, except that as it grows older the vine will be able to

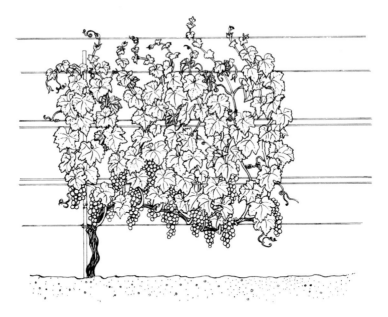

Double Guyot: the vine in its third season, with laterals bearing grapes

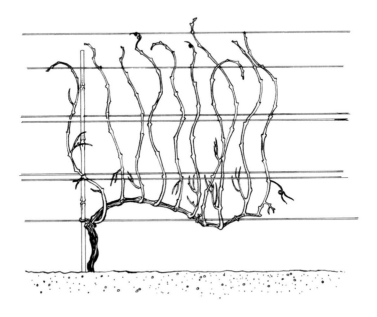

Double Guyot: the vine after leaf fall, at the end of the third season

carry a heavier crop of fruit. Each winter two canes are tied down and
a third cane is spur pruned to provide replacement canes.

In spring, at bud-burst, any buds which come from the stem of the
vine (watershoots) are rubbed off. As the years go by, however, the
stem of the vine tends to reach higher and higher from the ground. So,
occasionally, use can be made of a bud from the old wood of the stem,
which is more or less level with the bottom wire, to create a spur for
replacement canes.

Sometimes the vine will fail to provide strong, well ripened wood for
the replacement canes, perhaps because it has cropped too heavily to
make good growth, or because the summer has not been kind enough
to ripen the wood. If this happens, spur pruning of the laterals to two
buds can be done instead of the normal routine of cutting away last
season's fruiting canes.

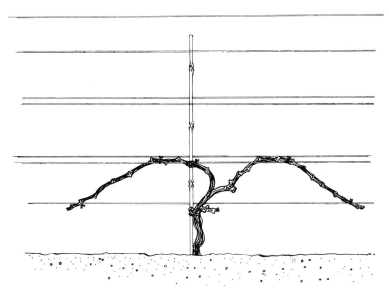

Double Guyot: from the third year, two canes are retained to bear the fruit and
one spur is retained to provide replacement canes for the following year

Sometimes two cane-bearing wires are used at the bottom of the
trellis, the second being about 150 mm (6 inches) above the lower. The
canes.are arched over the second wire and tied down to the bottom wire,
thus encouraging an even distribution of sap and discouraging the vine
from fruiting only towards the tip of the cane. One grower told me that
he had experimented with this method and had found it made no

difference to the fruiting. He prefers to tie the cane horizontally along one cane-bearing wire, as this simplifies the trimming of the laterals in late summer and also he saves on the extra wiring. Other growers believe strongly in arched canes and find it helpful to have a very sharp bend in the cane, almost to breaking point. This is a matter for experiment by the viticulturist to find out which method suits his vines.

Vines should never overlap so arching would suit vigorous varieties.

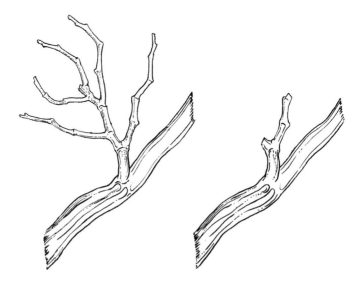

Spur pruning: the spur which has borne the fruit (on left) is pruned back to two buds (on right) or more, according to the variety of vine

Variations of the Double Guyot system

Growers can, and do, adapt the Guyot system to their own particular circumstances and to the preferences of their own vines on their own soil. The vines can be planted between 0.9 and 1.5 m (3–5 feet) apart in the rows; a vine planted in poor soil will not be able to fill such a large space so fruitfully as a vine planted in richer soil. The bottom wire can be set as low as 450 mm (18 inches) or as high as 900 mm (3 feet) or even higher and the trellis raised to take account of this. The distance between the rows varies between 1.5 and 2.7 m (5–9 feet) to take account of any machines that may be used.

The tendency in Britain is definitely towards higher vines, more widely spaced, than used to be the case. The reasons are: first, that wider spacing and higher vines help to increase the flow of air which

inhibits botrytis; second, that weed-killing sprays can be used around
the stems of high vines without harming the plants; third, that the work
of the vineyard is much less arduous if the vines are grown high enough
to avoid stooping; fourth, that the wider spacing and higher trellis
allow more leaf area to absorb sunlight and warmth; fifth, in commercial vineyards high labour costs make it essential for large machines
to be used between the rows; sixth, vines grown higher from the
ground are less vulnerable to frost damage.

Some growers, however, still prefer a more intensive system which
may suit poor soils, exposed positions, or small unmechanized family
concerns. Various intensive French methods are being tried out at
Hambledon in Hampshire and can be seen there.

SINGLE GUYOT

Single Guyot is well suited to a more intensive layout. It is carried out
exactly as Double Guyot except that only one cane is selected and tied
down each year, and one other cane is spur pruned to two buds,
growing two canes, of which the stronger will be tied down in the
following winter and the other discarded.

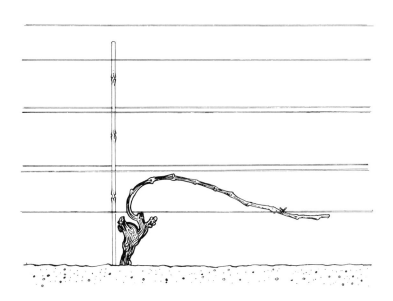

Single Guyot

GOBLET PRUNING

This is a system which as far as I know is not used commercially in Britain but has a certain appeal as it does away with the need for a post and wire trellis. It can be quite a trudge moving across a vineyard and I have found myself either diving under the bottom wires, or longing for a super-powered pogo stick.

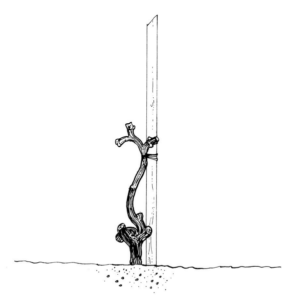

Goblet pruning: the pruned vine after its second season

With goblet pruning the only support for the vine is a stout tall stake. The newly planted vine is allowed to grow only one cane in its first year, as for Guyot pruning. In the second year again only one cane is grown and this is cut back to 450 mm (18 inches) above the ground in the following winter. In the third year only the top three buds are allowed to grow and these shoots are loosely tied in to the stake. Bunches of grapes may appear; three or four bunches, at the most, can be allowed to develop.

The shoots are spur pruned to two buds each in the following winter, so that in the fourth year there will be six canes, which can be allowed to carry one bunch of grapes each and are loosely tied in to the stake, as in the year before.

The following winter, these shoots are spur pruned to two buds and from this time on the strongest six to nine shoots are selected to grow each spring and the remaining shoots removed.

Goblet pruning: the vine is allowed to carry three fruiting canes in its third season

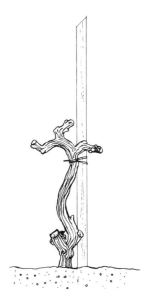

Goblet pruning: after the third season the three spurs are pruned to two buds

Summer pruning consists of pinching out the sublaterals and spur pruning to two buds is done each winter. This system is being experimentally used, with other systems, at Wye College in Kent but has not been in operation long enough for any conclusion to be drawn.

Of the various other ways of training vines, it is worth mentioning the *Lenz Moser system* which takes the vines high off the ground; the vines are planted 1.2 m (4 feet) apart with 2.7 m (9 feet) between the rows; the bottom wire is 1.2 m (4 feet) from the ground; the stem of the vine is grown up to this level and a cane tied down to the bottom wire on each side of the vines. The laterals shoot upwards; some are tied in to wires set at 1.5 m (5 feet) and 1.8 m (6 feet) above the ground, while the remainder hang down on either side.

Another variation is the *Double Arch* in which the stem of the vine is grown to 685 mm (2 feet 3 inches) above the ground. Two canes, one on each side of the vine, are bent sharply over a training wire at 1070 mm (3 feet 6 inches) above ground and tied down to a bottom wire 685 mm (2 feet 3 inches) above ground. This method is somewhat difficult to

Goblet pruning: the vine in its fourth season, carrying six fruiting canes

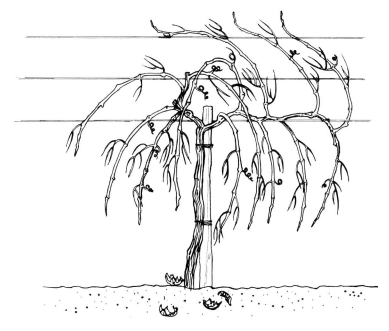

Lenz Moser system: vines grown on a high trellis, with roughly one-third of growth being trained up the wires and the remaining two-thirds being allowed to trail down on either side, thus giving maximum exposure to air and sun

establish, as the canes are apt to resent the sharp bending necessary and some snap. However, it does give more space to each cane so that the vines can be planted 1.2 m (4 feet) apart and can support twenty to twenty-four buds and yet have an air space of 75 mm (3 inches) between the canes of neighbouring plants.

Geneva Double Curtain

This is fundamentally different from the other systems so far considered. The object of all pruning systems is to produce as much healthy, good-quality fruit as possible. Guyot and most other systems achieve this through severely restricting growth while Geneva Double Curtain encourages, though it controls, growth. No summer pruning is required and there is no restriction of the number of spurs or the weight of the crop. The vine is given plenty of room and fed both with artificial fertilizers and with farmyard manure. This enables it to grow vigorously and crop as freely as it feels inclined. Grown in this way, vines appear to be self-regulating and will not overcrop.

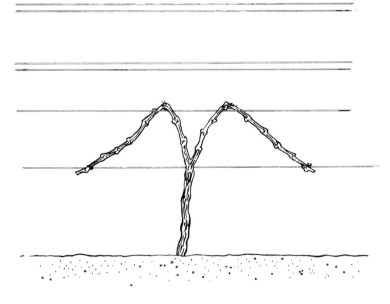

Double Arch: vine pruned and tied down

FIRST YEAR

The vines are planted 2.4 m (8 feet) apart in rows 3.6 m (12 feet) apart. They are pruned to two buds and planted in a strip of black polythene 1 m wide.

When the shoots appear, the strongest is selected to grow and any other shoots are removed. The cane may reach a height of 1.5–1.8 m (5–6 feet) in the first summer. Any laterals are left to grow, unrestricted.

In winter the vine is cut back to only two buds and the post and wire trellis erected. The T-shaped posts carry the two 9 gauge (or 3.75 mm) wires, 1.2 m (4 feet) apart, at a height of between 1.5 and 1.8 m (5–6 feet) above the ground.

SECOND YEAR

Once again, only one cane is allowed to grow and this year it will reach the wires. The vines are trained alternately to the left-hand and the right-hand wire.

When the vine reaches the wire, the leading shoot is pinched out and the laterals start to grow along the wire. All side shoots are pinched out from the stem and from the laterals growing along the wires, so that the vine's energy is concentrated on making as much growth as possible.

In the winter the laterals are cut back to the top of the stem, unless they are as thick as a pencil and the wood has ripened, in which case they can be left and will provide fruit in the following year.

THIRD YEAR

The laterals are allowed to grow along the wires so that each vine now has two branches 2.4 m (8 feet) long, one one each side. In this, the year of the first crop, the fruit will be borne on the branches.

In the winter the side shoots from the branches are spur pruned to two buds.

FOURTH YEAR

Each spur puts out two shoots of which the stronger is left to grow fruit and the other is removed.

The above is the basic system. Mr Bernard Theobald, who is the chief exponent of Geneva Double Curtain in Britain, is still experimenting and he says that it is better not to be too dogmatic. He says: 'A modification is being tried with a new planting which gives each vine four arms – two on each wire – each 1.2 m (4 feet) long, thus giving a better balance. As with the Lenz Moser system, it is possible to vary the pruning and use partial cane replacement or a combination of cane replacement and spur pruning. For example, Madeleine Angevine, a very vigorous plant, may benefit from leaving some long canes with four to six buds.'

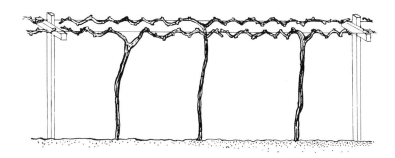

Geneva Double Curtain system

CHAPTER EIGHT

🌿 *The Vine and its Enemies*

The British Isles may not have the ideal climate for vines, but we are spared many of the scourges that afflict the traditional vine-growing lands. There are a host of viruses, bacteria, fungi and insects that prosper and multiply in countries where for miles vines are virtually the only crop. Vine soil-sickness and the pests which are common in such areas are largely unknown to us. The main troubles we have are due to our damp climate, which encourages various fungi.

An adequate programme of spraying fungicides is essential. The fungicides protect vines against infection but are unable to cure them once the infection has entered, so timing is the key to successful control of fungal diseases and this timing must be at its most accurate at around the time of flowering. This is a point to remember when planting vines of different varieties which come into flower at different dates.

Diseases

The most important diseases of vines in Britain are botrytis, oidium (powdery mildew) and phomopsis (dead arm).

BOTRYTIS (grey mould)

This is the worst of them all, and in a damp year its control is not easy. It is found everywhere and attacks a great many fruit and vegetable crops, being familiar to anyone who grows strawberries or raspberries and has found them rotting and covered with a whiskery mould. It flourishes in wet weather.

Botrytis attacks leaves of vines, appearing as a large brown blotch on the leaf, and stems, on which black spots are seen, usually towards the tips. Infected cane should be removed and burnt at pruning time. Most serious is infection of the fruit; the grapes rot, becoming covered with a mass of woolly grey mould. Botrytis cannot penetrate healthy plant tissues without some help; it must enter through a wound, which can be minute, or it can infect through dead or dying plant tissue. The most common time for the fruit to be infected is at flowering, when the little flower caps can fail to fall off the embryo berries, particularly if the weather is cool and damp at this time.

Spraying against botrytis takes place:
1   Just before flowering.
2   Just after flowering (usually defined as the moment when 80 per cent of the flower caps have fallen).
3   Before the growing grapes bunch up close together.
4   At the beginning of the ripening period.

From then on, spraying is repeated as necessary. In the very wet summer of 1977, Mr Carcary, the manager at Hambledon Vineyard, sprayed the vine seventeen times between July and November and feels that he saved the crop. In such cases, however, it is important to remember that there are minimum safety intervals between applying the last spray and harvesting; these intervals vary depending on the type of spray used.

If the vines are damaged by storms, botrytis can infect the canes very easily and overwinter within the plant. A winter spray with DNOC or tar-oil winter wash can control this source of infection.

OIDIUM (powdery mildew)

This fungus came to Europe from America and was first noticed at Kew Gardens in about 1850. Unlike botrytis, oidium likes dry, warm weather and vines which are suffering stress from drought are particularly vulnerable. It attacks early in the year and can be recognized by the white, dusty deposit which appears over the infected leaves and the fruit, which splits open providing an ideal opportunity for botrytis infection.

Spraying begins early, when the shoots are no more than 150 mm (6 inches) long and continues every ten to fourteen days until flowering, and after flowering if necessary. Sulphur is the good, traditional, cheap treatment for oidium. Dusting with sulphur is as effective as spraying if done in still, humid weather.

Oidium can take up to three weeks to show itself after entering the plant, if the weather is cool. The key to avoiding oidium is to spray early before any symptoms appear.

DEAD ARM (phomopsis)

This disease seems to be more of a problem than it used to be, especially in south-east England. The reasons for this are not understood; it is apparently common in a harmless form and it seems possible that it is sometimes a symptom rather than a cause of disease, for it spreads very rapidly through dying wood. It can be recognized by canes which are bleached white and have black spots; it is the bleaching which is the main thing to look out for, as healthy vines are also spotted.

Phomopsis is active in the winter and spring; the fungus does not develop much once the weather warms up. It is quite easily controlled by using DNOC in the winter, and by spraying at bud-burst, with a second spray a fortnight later if necessary.

DOWNY MILDEW (plasmopara)

Plasmopara is another unwelcome import from America. It was first identified in Europe in 1878 and it is troublesome in Europe but fortunately very rare in Britain. Indeed, some suspect that most reports of its appearance here are cases that have been wrongly identified.

Plasmopara shows itself as a white deposit on the underside of the leaves. It infects and destroys leaves and fruit. It flourishes in warm, damp weather and, once it has made an appearance, can persist for years in the soil.

Preventive spraying against plasmopara is considered worth while; the regular spraying programme against other fungi is generally quite adequate for this.

ARMILLARIA

Armillaria is a fungus which infects roots. Roots, left in the soil after clearing a site for vines, can be a source of infection but it is clearly difficult, if not impossible, to remove them completely.

There is no treatment. Major Gillespie of Wootton Vineyards told me that he has lost a few vines from armillaria. He has dug up the infected vines and left a space where they were, because, if new vines were planted, they would most probably become infected. The disease does not seem to have spread and he is not unduly worried about it.

VIRUS DISEASES

Virus diseases have not yet caused much trouble in Britain, but the position may well alter. Descriptions of the various virus diseases and their symptoms are given in specialist books. The only possible precaution is to buy virus-free stock.

Spraying Programme

Table 1 gives a spraying programme for vineyards and Table 2 gives a list of fungicides and their effectiveness against the vine maladies. The programme is as suitable for vines in the garden as for vineyards, but unfortunately not all the fungicides are available in small quantities. Zineb (for phomopsis and downy mildew) and sulphur (for oidium) are freely available; of the anti-botrytis sprays, Benlate can be obtained from most agricultural merchants. Zineb is diluted at the rate of 15 g to 5 litres ($\frac{1}{2}$ oz to the gallon) and wettable sulphur at 10 g to 5 litres ($\frac{1}{3}$ oz to the gallon).

TABLE 1. A Recommended Spraying Programme for Vineyards

Application rate: 1350–1700 litres per hectare (120–150 gallons per acre). Note: In many vineyards spraying takes place more frequently than in this programme, every ten to fourteen days, or even, in poor conditions, once a week.

	Time of Application	Materials	Additives	Purpose
1	December/February	DNOC (Sandolin) Dinoseb or Mortegg Emulsion (tar oil)	—	Dead arm, (Phomopsis viticola)
2	Budburst (large woolly bud)	Captan	Wetting agent	Dead arm (Phomopsis viticola)
3	Leaves about 25 mm (1 inch) in diameter (mid-May)	Antracol (propineb) or Dithane Vetra (mancozeb)	Wetting agent	Plasmopara (downy mildew)
4	Two to three weeks later	Propineb or mancozeb plus wettable sulphur (Spersul)	Wetting agent	Plasmopara and oidium (powdery mildew)
5	Two to three weeks later	Propineb or mancozeb plus wettable sulphur	Wetting agent	Plasmopara and oidium

| 6 | Two to three weeks later | Propineb or mancozeb and wettable sulphur plus Sumisclex*, Ronilan or Rovral | Wetting agent | Plasmopara, oidium and botrytis |

Flowering period – avoid spraying if possible (but not more than 14 days)

7	Two to three weeks later	Propineb or mancozeb and wettable sulphur plus Sumisclex, Ronilan or Rovral	Wetting agent	Plasmopara, oidium and botrytis
8	Two to three weeks later	Propineb or mancozeb and wettable sulphur plus Sumisclex, Ronilan or Rovral	Wetting agent	Plasmopara, oidium and botrytis
9	Two to three weeks later	Propineb or mancozeb and wettable sulphur plus Sumisclex, Ronilan or Rovral and malathion	Wetting agent	Plasmopora, oidium, botrytis and red spider
10	Two to three weeks later	Sumisclex, Ronilan or Rovral		Botrytis

The most important anti-botrytis spray is that which immediately follows flowering.

Rovral is obtainable from May and Baker Ltd. Rubigan, a new fungicide (Elanco), claimed to be active against powdery mildew, is being evaluated at the time of writing at Chilsdown Vineyard in West Sussex.

The method of spraying and dusting must be effective to give the necessary coverage; the sprays must penetrate right into the plants and cover the undersides as well as the tops of the leaves. Commercial growers are advised to use mist blower sprays which lift up the leaves by the force of the jet. The machine should be checked before use to see that it is working at full efficiency.

Smaller growers generally use a knapsack sprayer, costing around £35. These sprayers are very efficient but they are heavy to carry when full. Mr Farrar of Wye College points out that they cannot spray as finely as the mechanized blower sprays and that therefore far more of the liquid is applied to each plant. His advice is to use fungicides at half the recommended strength when using a knapsack sprayer.

* Sumisclex is not yet 'cleared' for use on any crop in the UK; it is being used experimentally on a small scale.

TABLE 2. Effectiveness of Fungicides for Vines

Fungicide		Grey mould (botrytis)	Powdery mildew (oidium)	Downy mildew (plasmopara)	Dead arm (phomopsis)
Daconil	A	+	(+)	+	+
Dinocap	A	−	+	−	−
Sulphur	A	−	+	−	−
Zineb	A	−	−	+	+
Antracol		−	−	+	+
Captan		(+)	−	+	+
Copper		−	(+)	+	+
Elvaron	A	+	(+)	+	+
Mancozeb		−	−	+	+
MBC-type		+	+	−	+
Thiram		+	−	+	+

A approved by the Ministry of Agriculture's Agricultural Chemical Approval Scheme.
+ active
(+) some effect
− no effect

Note: MBC-type fungicides (Bavistin, Benlate, Derosal, Mildothane and Tecto) are not effective where strains of botrytis tolerant of these chemicals occur. This information was supplied by Mr Upstone, formerly plant pathologist at the ADAS Sub-centre at Wye.

For dusting with sulphur, there is a small, Japanese hand-held sulphur machine on the market which is satisfactory for dusting small vineyards. It has to be refilled too frequently to be efficient in larger vineyards of perhaps an acre or more and a larger machine would have to be used.

No one whose livelihood depends on a vineyard can afford to take chances with the spraying programme, which generally begins as soon as the newly planted vines start to grow and is followed religiously year by year. Mr Farrar told me that at his experimental vineyard at Wye College the spraying does not take place as frequently as it does in some commercial vineyards, 'But I can't advise them to copy me; they couldn't take the risk.'

Risks can perhaps be taken with family vineyards. It may not be necessary to spray vines in the first year and one successful grower, Mrs Pamela Smith, who runs Flexerne vineyard in East Sussex on very do-it-yourself and economical lines, managed to avoid fungicides altogether, with the exception of dusting with sulphur and Bordeaux mixture, for years until the very wet summer of 1977.

Spraying with fungicides is not done near to harvesting and the period following the end of spraying is apt to become a race between botrytis and ripening. Spraying ceases because fungicides have a bad effect on winemaking. As Michael Waterfield reported in the English Vineyards Association journal, 'With regard to vinification I have found without a doubt that fungicides affect and slow down fermentation.' Opinions differ somewhat on how long a period should elapse between the last spraying and harvest. The manufacturers' instructions do not give any guidance for winemakers; they apply only to crops for direct human consumption. Three weeks would appear to be the minimum interval, but at Lamberhurst Priory no spraying takes place for six weeks before harvest.

Insect pests

PHYLLOXERA

Phylloxera, the vine louse, which very nearly made the European vine extinct, is so far not a problem in the British Isles but should not be ignored. Phylloxera likes a humid climate. An outbreak in one place can infect vineyards a distance of twenty or thirty miles away. There is no cure, but vines grafted on to American rootstocks are resistant to phylloxera. So both the disease and its remedy have come from the USA.

WASPS

Wasps are a nuisance particularly with early ripening varieties. They can be kept down to a limited extent by taking any nests which are seen and by the use of wasp traps – jam jars half filled with a sweet liquid which attracts the wasps and then drowns them. There is an insecticide, produced by Murphy Chemical Ltd, for the protection of fruit kept in store. If sprayed on to the grapes every fortnight while wasps are troublesome, this spray, Murvin 85, will deal with them. Murvin 85 (Carbaryl) is cleared for use on vines up to 7 days before harvest. Mr Theobald of Westbury Farm, who grows some early varieties, was recommended to try this spray and has found that it works. Certain nets also discourage wasps – see page 64.

RED SPIDER

Red spider may affect vines. Malathion, or derris sprayed on the leaves
of the vines, will control this pest.

Birds

'We heard a few blackbirds clucking about one evening – the next day
there wasn't one grape left,' said one grower. Blackbirds and thrushes
are the chief villains; starlings can also be a problem.

Bird scarers and broadcasts of bird distress calls seem to be almost
useless against bird damage. Nets are an expensive, but effective,
protection. There are three types. One is a fine mesh which comes in
200 m rolls and is 1 m wide. It can be hung over the fruit, using one
strip each side of the row and securing the strips together with clips.
This netting is fine enough to give some protection against wasps as
well as birds and if it can be blue it deters the wasps more effectively.
Unfortunately, it is not made in blue in this country and Lamberhurst
Priory Vineyard, which uses this netting, and acts as agent for it in the
UK, imports it from Germany for this reason. There is a yellow,
light-weight, plastic netting which is used only once and thrown away.
It is called Xironet, and is available from Compact Packaging Ltd,
of St Albans, Hertfordshire.

The third type of netting is hung right over the top of the entire
vineyard on supporting wires stretched between high stakes at the top
of the trellis. One-inch Lobrene netting, which can be ordered from
Low Brothers and Co. of Dundee, is the type most commonly used. It
is light, soft and strong. It is resistant to ultra-violet breakdown and
should therefore last for five or even ten years with care. Holes can be
mended with polypropylene twine; damage is usually caused by high
winds and the nets are most vulnerable where they are supported by the
posts. Polythene bags tied over the tops of the posts reduce the risk of
damage. More unusual damage has been reported from Cherrybank
Vineyard in Suffolk, whose stored nets were chewed by rats; they
recommend hanging rolled-up nets from a ceiling or else keeping them
in rat-proof containers. At Wye Vineyard the job of taking down the
nets was put off rather too long one year; a heavy, early fall of snow
did a great deal of harm to the nets which were, however, mended
successfully and almost invisibly by polypropylene twine.

Putting up and taking down large nets is a daunting job, particularly on a wet day when showers of small drops from the netting fall

down the necks of the unhappy workers. The method is to roll up the net and take it to the end of the vineyard, where it is laid out like a long sausage. It is then rolled over the rows, rather like laying a carpet. Buckles and buttons catch in the nets so clothing should be as smooth as possible. One year when doing this job two of us lost an ear stud in the nets.

Pamela Smith, who, as I have mentioned, has a vineyard which she manages more or less on her own, finds that it takes her a week to net her 2½-acre vineyard. Each of her nets covers a quarter of an acre. Another grower had worked out that it takes two people a whole day to net 1 acre. At Penshurst Vineyard, six or seven people netted 3 acres in five hours; many hands made light work. In this vineyard the nets had been sewn together to make one gigantic net which saved much time, but made the net somewhat difficult to straighten out so that it would hang down to the ground on all sides.

Another method of joining nets together without sewing is to run single-strand barbed wire along the rows where two nets meet and along the outside rows. The nets are then held taut on the barbs. This is done by Cherrybank Estates in Suffolk and Mr Robin Don of Elmham in Norfolk.

Just before netting, which should be done as soon as the grapes begin to ripen in September or thereabouts, all protruding vine shoots and any tendrils which may have attached themselves to the top, net-bearing wires are removed and spraying, cultivating or mowing jobs are done. Some grass-cutting machines slash the pruned shoots into chaff, which is a convenient way to dispose of them.

The expense of netting large areas is considerable and many large-scale growers feel that it cannot be justified. Black cotton could be the answer. Mr Barnes of Little Whatmans Vineyard, at Biddenden in Kent, puts two threads of cotton around the rows underneath the fruit and two threads over the fruit, and finds that this deters blackbirds and thrushes, which like to approach the feast from below. Flocks of star-lings pay much less attention to the cotton, but at least they can be seen as they come and kept at bay by warning shots. Black cotton, supplemented by walking round with a gun, is also used by Mr Theobald at Westbury. Both these vineyards are large and Mr Barnes is an apple-grower as well as a vine-grower, so neither of these vineyards is as vulnerable as small vineyards in areas where little other fruit is grown; such vineyards attract birds from far and wide. However, the black cotton is so cheap that it could be worth a try: Mr Barnes

calculated it cost him only £35 to black-thread 7 acres. Where black
cotton is used it should be carefully removed before harvest, or it will
tend to appear in the grape crusher. Mr Barnes feels that the method
is so cheap and so effective that he is happy to cope with this one
inconvenience.

PIGEONS AND PHEASANTS

Pigeons can occasionally go for young vine leaves and shoots. A walk
around with a gun is the best way to deal with them. Pheasants can be
a problem and if the vineyard is on rented land, the vine-grower may
find that his landlord objects to him shooting them. It is advised that
in such cases the grower sorts this out with his landlord at the beginning
of the lease if possible, or at any rate at an early stage. Many landowners and syndicates invest a lot of money in their shoots and are
probably not aware of the problems of vine-growing, so an amicable
discussion could avert trouble.

Frost

Vines are fairly hardy while dormant, but a spring frost can kill young
shoots and September frosts can cause the vines to shed their leaves too
early, while they should still be doing their job as sugar factories for the
ripening fruit. Frost-prone sites should be avoided. If a frost is forecast,
the vines can be given some protection by an evening sprinkling with
water. On a small scale, polythene or other protection can be draped
over the vines.

Weeds

Weeds are also enemies of the vine and can delay cropping for a year
or more if not dealt with; sprays used against them could be more
damaging than the weeds if badly chosen or wrongly used. A neighbour
of ours, who has recently moved into a house with a neglected garden,
attempted to solve her weed problem by dowsing it with a selective
weed-killer. She now has no weeds but nothing else will grow either.
The proliferation of weed-killers under various trade names is extremely
confusing and even the experts have a hard time to keep up with
developments. Chemical companies do not market weed-killers with
vines in mind, so there is not much help from the makers' instructions.
    There are three basic types of weed-killers: those incorporating

dalapon, which are used against couch-grass; residual herbicides such as simazine, which leave a herbicide film over the soil surface, and contact herbicides, which include hormone herbicides. Tried and tested in vineyards are paraquat and Gramoxone (which is paraquat based); these kill only green foliage and are neutralized when they reach the soil, so that they have no effect on roots or ripe wood. Paraquat is often used before planting and for weed control in between the vines themselves when they are large enough. Simazine is also much used to supplement Gramoxone, as are Casoron G granules which, however, must not be used for the first three years in a new vineyard. Indeed, it is always better not to spray any herbicides around young vines, although some growers get away with it. The weed-killer Round-up is much used in vineyards and is very effective against nearly all weeds and especially against thistles.

Round-up, being systemic, must not touch the vine foliage or it will be drawn into the system of the plant; it is used while the vines are dormant and is 'spotted' over the vineyard where needed. It is fully cleared for use in orchards and for soft fruits. Another herbicide, Ronstar, is recommended for bindweed.

Total herbiciding eventually produces a mossy surface full of cracks and fissures which provide natural drainage; it is not unattractive and can be seen in any field of blackcurrants as well as in the vineyards which use this method.

More traditional weapons against weeds are the hoe and the cultivator. Most growers use a hoe to cope with weeds between the vines for the first three years, unless the vines were planted in black polythene (see page 35). Cultivators can be used in the lanes between the rows, but are apt to damage the vine roots, particularly in shallow soils. They also disturb the soil structure and make it more difficult to get on the vineyard in wet weather.

In some parts of the country, particularly where corn is grown, some unwelcome herbicides may come drifting over the fence. Vines are sensitive to fumes from hormone weed-killers which affect their leaves and growth. Some research into this is being carried out at Wye College, where it is felt that the seriousness of the damage may be rather overestimated; yet it is a distressing sight to see vine leaves warped and distorted, and many commercial growers feel that such damage has affected their crops badly.

In New Zealand, regulations ban the use of hormone preparations, in the growing season, within five miles of a vineyard if sprayed from the air and within one to five miles of a vineyard if sprayed from the ground; they also restrict the use of hormone on vines, even when they are dormant.

The fumes can be carried on to the vines by the wind, or, more insidiously, by thermal currents on the warm still days that a farmer might think were 'safe' for spraying without drift. A gentle breeze blowing away from the vines would be better plus the use of the less fumy herbicides. Friendly discussion with neighbours is essential. Claims for damage are very difficult to establish.

CHAPTER NINE

❦ *Feeding the Vines*

The aim of fertilizing is to have a balanced, fruitful soil; as with people, over-feeding is almost as bad as under-feeding and the proportions must be right. The acid-alkali balance must be corrected by liming, if necessary; the vital nutrients of nitrogen, potash and phosphates must be present in the correct amounts and trace elements, those minute but essential quantities of certain minerals, may need to be adjusted. There must also be enough humus in the soil to keep it friable, moist and alive, to allow a good run for the roots.

Vines in the garden

Soil analysis and leaf analysis will show the needs of the soil and the vines, but a close eye on the look of the plants will reveal a great deal of information and the gardener with just a few vines will probably rely almost entirely on these visual signs.

If the vines are growing well, with healthy green leaves, and the canes are as thick as a pencil, then there will be no shortage of nitrogen, which reveals itself in poor growth and pale leaves.

If the canes are thick and sappy and the leaves oversized and dark green, then there is probably too much nitrogen in the soil.

If the older leaves are discoloured and bluish, this is a sign of phosphate deficiency.

If the leaves go brown at the edges and start to die back, potash deficiency can be the culprit.

If the leaves turn yellow in the summer then probably the vines are unable to take up enough iron from the soil, due either to a shortage of magnesium or to an over-limy soil. An iron preparation, such as Sequestrene, will cure the symptoms; soil analysis will show the cause, which can then be treated. A shortage of magnesium can be cured by liming, when appropriate, with high-grade magnesian limestone, or by applying Epsom salts either to the soil or as a foliar spray.

It is impossible to be dogmatic about fertilizers. So much depends on the state of the soil and on whether farmyard manure is used as well as artificial fertilizers and in what quantities. Nitrogen is particularly tricky, for the amount necessary will vary according to the rainfall, amount of organic material in the soil and cultivation methods. Vines in areas of heavy rainfall may need only half as much nitrogen as those in drier parts of the country. If the vines are grown in weeded strips between grass lanes, they will need about 25 per cent more nitrogen than those grown in completely weed-free soil. Young small vines will need less feeding than large mature plants in full production. The suggestions below are intended as a rough guide only.

Fertilizers for vines in the garden

In spring, apply:

Nitrogen (N). 35 g of sulphate of ammonia per square metre
($1\frac{1}{2}$ oz per square yard)
Phosphate (P or P_2O_5). 25 g of superphosphate per square metre
(1 oz per square yard)
Potash (K or K_2O). 50 g of sulphate of potash per square metre
(2 oz per square yard)
Farmyard manure or good compost. About five large spadefuls per vine, spread widely around the plant.

In autumn, soils with a pH below 6.5 will need liming every two or three years, using about 100 g lime per square metre (4 oz per square yard).

These amounts should be adequate for soil in reasonably good heart, but it may be that the vines will not flourish. The most common cause of unhappiness in vines is not poor feeding but poor drainage; if this is definitely not the trouble, but the vines still look miserable, then ADAS should probably be asked to come to analyse the soil, so that any imbalance can be put right.

Fertilizers for the larger vineyard

Soil analysis every four to five years is essential for a vineyard of any size and the Ministry of Agriculture recommendations are based on a soil analysis report. For each nutrient the report gives an index figure representing the amount of nutrient in the soil. In the case of nitrogen there is no satisfactory method of soil analysis. Nitrogen recommendations are based on the quantity of summer rainfall and on the cultivation methods used in the vineyard.

For the time being ADAS is recommending the same fertilizers for vines as for raspberries; these are more or less the same as those used in Germany for vines and are thus probably suitable for vines in the United Kingdom. Meanwhile research is going on at Efford in Hampshire on nutrition for vines, but unfortunately no results are yet available. However, it seems from comments both from growers and from some ADAS officers that if the recommendations err it is to be rather on the mean side, particularly where potash is concerned.

Amounts in the following notes are not given in pounds per acre as fertilizer bags have gone metric. 50 kg bags of fertilizer have the percentage of each nutrient stamped on the bag and so to work out how many kilograms of a given nutrient are in the bag it is only necessary to divide the percentage by two. For example a 50 kg bag with 19 per cent superphosphate contains 9.5 kg of this nutrient.

LIME

Liming requirements are given in the soil analysis report in tonnes per hectare and should be carefully followed, as overliming is extremely harmful. If the magnesium index shows a deficiency, with a figure of 2 or lower, the lime should be added in the form of high-grade magnesium limestone, otherwise as finely ground chalk or ground limestone.

NITROGEN (N)

Vines in drier areas, with a summer rainfall below 355 mm (14 inches), need 100 kg per hectare/$2\frac{1}{2}$ acres (75 kg per hectare/$2\frac{1}{2}$ acres after establishment).

Vines in wetter areas, with a summer rainfall above 355 mm (14 inches), need less nitrogen. In these areas 50 kg per hectare/$2\frac{1}{2}$ acres (25 kg per hectare/$2\frac{1}{2}$ acres after establishment) should be applied.

If the vines are planted between grass lanes, the amounts should be increased by perhaps 25 kg per hectare/$2\frac{1}{2}$ acres.

PHOSPHATE (P or P_2O_5)

Index	0	1	2	3	over 3
kg per hectare/$2\frac{1}{2}$ acres	110	75	40	40	—

POTASH (K or K₂O)

Index	0	1	2	3	over 3
kg per hectare/2½ acres	310	250	190	125	—

Soil samples are taken at two levels, one near the surface and one between 150 and 300 mm (6–12 inches) deep. If the deeper sample shows a deficiency of potash, with an index of 0, then the amounts of potash applied should be increased by 60 kg per hectare/2½ acres.

MAGNESIUM (Mg)

Index	0	1	2	over 2
kg per hectare/2½ acres	60	40	30	—

FARMYARD MANURE

If farmyard manure is put on the vineyard at the rate of 25 tonnes per hectare (10 tonnes per acre), the above amounts of fertilizers per hectare should be reduced by 35 kg of nitrogen, 50 kg of phosphate, 95 kg of potash and 20 kg of magnesium.

If no soil report is available, apply 40 kg of phosphate and 125 kg of potash per hectare with the appropriate amount of nitrogen, but no magnesium should be applied.

TO CORRECT TRACE-ELEMENT DEFICIENCIES

Iron. Sequestrene 138 Fe is dissolved in water and added to the soil in early February at a rate of 10 g per square metre (¼ oz per square yard) or is used as a foliar spray at 1 kg per 1000 litres of water (1 lb per 100 gallons) fortnightly through the season.

Manganese. 4 kg of manganese sulphate diluted in at least 1000 litres of water per hectare (4 lb in at least 100 gallons per acre). The treatment may have to be repeated.

Boron. 20 kg of borax per hectare (20 lb per acre) or, as a foliar spray, Solubor, applied at 2 kg per 1000 litres of water per hectare (2 lb per 100 gallons per acre).

Copper. 2 kg of copper oxychloride in at least 1000 litres of water per hectare (2 lb in at least 20 gallons of water per acre).

Trace-element toxicities may occur due to soil acidity or contamination; ADAS should be consulted.

Types of fertilizers

Fertilizers are sold in 50 kg bags either as a single nutrient or as a compound fertilizer containing several nutrients. Both are satisfactory. A water-soluble phosphate is the best type to use; for potash, sulphate of potash is recommended; all forms of nitrogen are equally effective. The cheapest form of magnesium is magnesian limestone; Epsom salts can also be used and are the only suitable form of magnesium for foliar spraying; 20 lb in 100 gallons of water are sprayed to the acre.

Foliar sprays are very highly spoken of by many growers who regularly use Maxicrop at 1 gallon to the acre as part of their general fertilizing programme. Sprays are also invaluable for correcting trace-element deficiencies, but Mr Heath of ADAS warns that it is far better to use the specific spray for the deficiency in question rather than to rely on an all-purpose spray which will probably not contain enough of what is really needed. Foliar sprays are most effective when allowed to dry slowly and spraying on a dull overcast day is recommended for this reason. In many vineyards manganese is sprayed, when necessary, mixed with fungicide to save labour and kill two birds with one stone.

When to apply fertilizers

Nitrogen must be used in the spring and/or summer after the fruit has set. Farmyard manure, compost, potash and phosphates can go on in autumn or in spring. Foliar sprays must of course be used in the leafy season.

Leaf analysis will become more and more useful as an aid for the grower anxious to know that the vines are getting exactly what they need. Mr Heath has given me the following advice which he says is 'rather tentative'; it is based on 'leaves taken from the mid-third of the extension growth between mid-August and mid-September', that is, leaves which are mature but not too old, and he emphasizes that these figures cannot be compared with any from the Continent, partly because there the stalk of the leaf is used for testing, while here the leaf itself is used.

Mr Heath's table is:	*Normal*	*Deficient*
N	3.0 to 3.5	less than 2.0
P	0.2 to 0.3	less than 0.15
K	1.3 to 1.5	less than 1.0
Mg	0.16 to 0.24	less than 0.13
Ca	0.8 to 1.0	less than 0.7

Sources of help with any nutritional problems are firstly, ADAS, who will do a soil analysis for anybody who is prepared to pay for it and also will give advice to those with commercial holdings, and secondly, local agricultural colleges, who may advise people with smaller holdings or gardens.

CHAPTER TEN

❧ *Harvest and Winemaking*

The grapes are picked as late as the weather will allow, in northern latitudes, for in many years the grapes will not ripen fully until late October or even early November, although some early varieties may ripen in mid-September. The risks of waiting are obvious; disease can attack the fruit, or heavy rain can dilute the sugar in the grapes, as happened so frustratingly in the 'great drought' year of 1976. This should have been a superb year, but many growers found that grapes harvested early were sweeter than those kept for a later harvest; crops were very heavy but quality was disappointing. A dry, warm October is what vine-growers pray for.

Large vineyards have to rely on paid labour for picking and it is not easy to re-arrange harvest dates to take quick advantage of a change in the weather. In smaller vineyards arrangements can be more flexible.

If the weather is good the grapes are left on the vines until they are swollen and transparent, looking almost ready to burst. Sugar readings are taken as the harvest date approaches. Professionals generally use a refractometer, a neat and expensive little instrument which gives a sugar reading from a sample drop of juice. A hydrometer can also be used. This is an instrument which gives a reading when floated in a sample of juice (which should not be pressed from the ripest grapes only!). It is also used for assessing the sugar content of the pressed juice when winemaking. One or two degrees are subtracted from the reading to allow for the debris in the juice and the anxious grower then has to decide whether to harvest or not.

A sugar content of 44° is the minimum allowed under EEC law, but the grapes would hardly be worth picking with a reading of less than 50°, and every grower would hope to do considerably better than that in a normal year. A reading of 70° to 75° would be perfect. If the season is late or the weather bad, he may have to harvest before the grapes have reached perfection. Vineyards in northern Europe have the same problem and yet manage to produce very good wines.

If the vineyard is big enough to need outside help, it will be found that for some reason people are willing, eager even, to pick grapes. Mrs Pamela Smith used to grow soft fruit and one of the factors that induced her to change to growing grapes was that she found it difficult to persuade people to pick her strawberries. There is no such problem with her grape harvest and her crop at Flexerne is picked by seven or eight people over four days; they start at first light and pick until dark, with meals provided to maintain their stamina.

At the Paget Brothers' much larger vineyard at Chilsdown, fifteen workers pick 4 tonnes of grapes a day. They pick into plastic boxes with a capacity of about $4\frac{1}{2}$–$5\frac{1}{2}$ kg (10–12 lb); large plastic containers (the Allibert 10 litre size, which contain exactly 1 cwt (50.8 kg) of grapes) are used to carry the grapes down the rows where they are loaded on to the waiting tractor and trailer.

All the professionals are adamant that it is essential to use paid helpers for harvesting. 'Friends arrive late and complain of backache.' This may well be true; I spoke to one friend who had been allowed to help. 'You have to pick on your knees,' she said. 'I was the first to use a kneepad.' This is a point in favour of growing grapes high above the ground; backache can thus be avoided.

The other hazard for pickers is the risk of cutting fingers instead of grape stalks; this is a common accident in vineyards. Special grape-cutting shears can be used and these are much safer than secateurs; alternatively, a good pair of scissors will do the job.

The picking is done in dry weather, if possible, and if there is time to wait until the dew is off the grapes, so much the better. No more grapes are picked than can be processed in that same day, for they deteriorate very quickly. This means that everything must be ready for the winemaking in plenty of time for the harvest. Any hold-ups could be fatal.

When the grapes have been harvested, and they are of as good quality and in as good condition as the grower has been able to achieve, he has contributed perhaps 50 per cent to the quality of the finished wine. The rest depends on the skill and care of the winemaker and it is here perhaps that there is most scope for the improvement of English wines. It was noticeable that at the three-day conference on the future of English wine at Wye College in September 1978 there was not one speaker on winemaking. This was a pity for, at the price it is now, English wine has to compete with good imported wines with established reputations. English wines are in somewhat the same position as women seeking responsible, well paid jobs in competition with men. It is not enough to be as good as the opposition, they must be, beyond any doubt, better.

Most vineyards can produce an honest, palatable wine. Some make wine of real excellence. With greater knowledge, experience and skill, standards will continue to rise, encouraged by competitions, trophies and awards which range from the international competitions to the award given annually to the best wines from vineyards of half an acre or less at the English Wine Festival, organized by Valley Wine Cellars of Alfriston, East Sussex.

Many Continental vine-growers would never dream of making wine themselves. They send their grapes to the local wine cooperatives where skilled workers, using up-to-date equipment, can produce wine very efficiently. There are no such cooperatives in Britain but the Merrydown Wine Company and also certain vineyards will make wine for other growers. None of these schemes is cooperative in the Continental sense, for each English vineyard retains its individuality by having its wine made separately from any other.* Details of the schemes vary. The Merrydown Wine Company will make wine for a cash payment or will accept a proportion of the crop or of the wine. Its scheme is financed partly by the growers who use it, for Merrydown asks growers to loan money to help pay for the necessary fermentation vats and containers; this money can be repaid when and if the grower wishes to leave the scheme. Pilton Manor in Somerset also makes wine for other growers. In this scheme growers buy their own storage containers and this is found to be a satisfactory arrangement.

Not all growers who use cooperatives produce wine in quantity. At present the Merrydown Company is willing to make wine in very small quantities for small trial vineyards and those not yet in full production, but Mr Jack Ward, the Chairman, is doubtful whether this can be continued indefinitely. Economically, it makes much better sense to use larger equipment and make large quantities of wine. At Lamberhurst Priory in Kent, the large, modern winery can handle quantities as small as 100 kg, but the extra trouble involved in making wine in

---

* Merrydown also make a wine that they call Anderida from blended grapes from several vineyards.

these small quantities is naturally reflected in the price charged to the grower.

In the winery at Wootton Vines in Somerset, 5 gallon and 10 gallon carboys can be seen beside the usual bulk fermentation vats. Major Gillespie uses the carboys for making wine for small growers, but he has found that 10 gallons (45 litres) is the minimum satisfactory quantity, if the quality is not to be sacrificed. Wine in small containers is more vulnerable to oxidation and to rapid temperature changes.

If the wine is to be made away from the vineyard, it is important to see that the grapes survive the journey to the winery in good condition. Nearly all those who make wine for others have some horror story to tell of ruined loads of grapes. All advise growers not to wrap the grapes in polythene but to pack them in wooden or Allibert plastic crates and to stack these in such a way that there is no pressure on the fruit. The grapes should reach the winery as soon as possible after picking. Merrydown has four wine presses in order that the grapes can be rushed to the press once they are delivered, but no amount of care at the winery can retrieve damage caused by faulty packing and delays on the journey.

Equipment

Whether a vineyard is large or small, the process of harvesting and winemaking is the same and the equipment varies chiefly in size and expense. This brief description is intended to help the amateur.

Even the smallest enterprise will need:

Polythene buckets for picking
Polythene bins, to hold and carry the grapes
Containers for fermentation and storage with bungs or corks to fit
Airlocks, and corks to fit them
Siphoning tubes
Funnels
A filter
A measuring jug
A hydrometer
An acid test-kit
A corking machine
Wine bottles and corks
Labels, collars and caps, if used
Wine yeast
Sugar

Sterilizing chemicals, such as Campden tablets (potassium
metabisulphate) or sodium metabisulphate
Finings, such as bentonite
Also helpful: A balance for weighing small quantities of chemicals
A pocket calculator
Essential for large crops: A wine press. A grape crusher.

If more than a few kilos of grapes are being produced then a wine press and grape crusher will be needed. Very small quantities can be 'pressed' by putting crushed grapes in a clean Terylene net curtain, which is then wrung out over a bucket, but obviously there is a limit to the amount that can be treated in this way. The grapes must be crushed before pressing; this can be done with the hands, for small quantities, or the grapes can be trodden in a tub in the time-honoured way. However, accidents can happen. One amateur winemaker trod his entire harvest of grapes in the bath. As he stepped out, he automatically pulled out the plug . . . .

The amount of money which can be spent on winemaking equipment is almost limitless and winemakers are most ingenious in adapting, making or finding cheap alternatives.

For home winemaking, wooden rollers from old-fashioned mangles can be set in a home-made wooden hopper and used for crushing grapes. Wine presses too, can be home-made, or they can still be acquired cheaply on the Continent. One small-scale grower found an old wine press when on holiday in Spain. He bought it for a song, dismantled it, brought it back on the roof-rack of his car and erected it in his garage. An ex-dairy farmer ferments his wine in the stainless-steel bulk container which once held milk. Second-hand or even third-hand equipment is on the market and can be a very good buy. Wooden casks can still be bought at a reasonable price on the Continent or can sometimes be acquired second-hand. Mr and Mrs Barrett at Felsted use ex-Madeira casks which they restore with great skill.

If new equipment is bought, one comforting thought is that most of it should last a lifetime and the amateur can also cheer himself by the consideration that much of the equipment can be used for making other drinks. For example, a wine press can also be used for pressing apples.

A list of suppliers of wine-making equipment is in Appendix 3.

The winery

The winery should have enough space to contain the fermentation carboys or casks plus a comfortably sized work surface for the various pieces of testing apparatus. It should also be easy to clean. Many amateurs manage to make good wine in a larder or spare bedroom, but a shed, garage or barn which can be washed down is preferable.

It should be cool, for the delicate fragrant bouquet of the white wines characteristic of the British Isles will be lost if the fermentation is too violent. At the start of the fermentation, a temperature of between 10 °C and 16 °C (50–60 °F) is to be aimed at. Once fermentation has started, a temperature of 4–10 °C (40–50 °F) is about right. The fermenting must gives off its own heat and so too warm a temperature in a winery is undesirable.

Fermenting wine also gives off carbon dioxide, so good ventilation, particularly when large quantities are involved, is essential.

Fermentation containers are best made of glass or wood, for the amateur. The professionals have their large modern fermentation vats but they, too, use glass carboys and wooden casks to hold their surplus wine, or, in some cases, small quantities of different wines.

The best casks are of oak, but chestnut is a cheaper alternative. Second-hand white-wine casks can sometimes be found; for white wine, ex-red-wine casks are not really suitable and ex-beer casks would definitely be a bad buy.

Wooden casks are rather a business to clean and maintain and they are heavy and awkward to handle, as anyone who has had to look after a wooden boat will readily appreciate. They must not be allowed to dry out, or the wood will shrink and leaks will appear, and they must be chocked up on four curved wooden supports or the weight will be too great for the bottom stave. When the casks arrive, they are cleaned, if necessary, before being chocked up off the ground with the bung hole at the top and filled with sulphited water (500 mg of SO_2 to 1 litre of water) until they are needed. Just before use, they are rinsed out with clean water.

To clean a dirty cask, put in a chain and some water and roll the barrel around until all traces of dirt are removed. If the cask smells sour and vinegary it will ruin the wine. In this case it is filled with water and left for two days. Then it is emptied and a caustic solution of sodium hydroxide – 125 g to 10 litres of boiling water (4 oz to 2 gallons) – is poured into the cask and swilled around it. This solution is left in the cask for twelve hours while the cask is turned every two hours to allow the solution to reach every part. It is then rinsed out very thoroughly with several changes of water, before sulphiting as described above. If the cask smells musty, 20 g of calcium chloride dissolved in 4.5 litres of water (0.7 oz in 1 gallon) is rolled around the inside of the cask, which is then left for two hours before rinsing thoroughly with water. If, after treatment, a cask still smells of anything except SO_2 it should not be used for making wine.

The advantages that casks have over glass carboys are, first, that they are available in much larger sizes and, second, that they make better wine.

Glass carboys and jars are in many sizes from ½ gallon to 10 gallons (2–45 litres). They are easy to clean and fairly easy to obtain, although there may be difficulty with the larger sizes and it is a good idea to buy these well in advance. Plastics are not recommended for fermentation and storage.

A press and a crusher are essential if the crop is to be of any size. Sometimes two or three families combine to share the expense of these large items, which is not totally satisfactory as they all tend to need them at the same time. They can be home-made or can be bought from various sources (see Appendix 3). Wine presses are made of oak, for strength, and all metal parts should be painted or varnished to prevent contamination. Moving parts are greased with Vaseline, which is tasteless.

Airlocks, siphoning tubes, funnels, jugs and the like are best made of plastic which lasts more or less for ever. Airlocks, and the bored corks to fit them, should be of an appropriate size for the fermentation vessel; a small airlock will not be adequate for a large container.

Items of equipment which may be needed for large quantities, such as a floor corking machine, a bottle-cleaning spray unit or large filter unit, can be hired and a family-sized vineyard might well produce enough grapes to make this worth while. For small crops, a cheap hand corker and a small filter are quite adequate, while bottles can be cleaned in the kitchen sink.

A hydrometer is essential for winemaking, first to establish the sugar content of the must and then to test whether the fermentation is complete and all the sugar has been converted to alcohol. It can also be used to test the grapes for sugar content before harvest, if the crop is big enough for a few bunches to be spared for the necessary pressing and testing. The gardener with a few vines will have to rely on the

taste and appearance of the grapes, which are not a very reliable guide,
unless he can borrow a refractometer which can test the juice from a
single grape.

Yeast

In Britain it is not advised to rely on the yeasts present in the bloom
on the grapes. This is far too risky so far north, although it is the way
that wine has been made for centuries and it is still made this way in
parts of Europe by traditionally minded farmers (there is an account
of traditional wine-making in France in Chapter 12). Here in Britain
the grape juice is sterilized with sulphur dioxide at the first possible
moment and yeast starter solution is introduced to ferment the wine
free from competition from undesirable wild yeasts and infections
which can spoil the vintage. Some growers are so anxious to avoid any
risks that the grapes are treated with sulphur dioxide as they are
picked, before they even reach the winery.

Wine yeasts are available in dried or liquid form; liquid yeasts are
preferable and are the only yeasts to perform well in the recommended
cool, slow fermentation. To make a starter solution, a couple of days
before harvest, $\frac{1}{2}$–1 litre (1–2 pints) of grape juice is pressed and then
sterilized by being heated to 85 °C (185 °F) and kept at this heat for a
few minutes. It is poured into a sterilized container, such as a bottle or
flask, and a wad of sterile cotton wool is used to plug the neck of the
container. When it has cooled, the yeast is added, the cotton wool
replaced and the solution is then kept in a warm place to incubate.

Professional winemakers use yeast cultures from the Continent which
are not generally available for amateurs. Suitable wine yeasts are
available from winemakers' shops; hock yeast for white wines and
Burgundy yeast for red wines would be appropriate. Only Loftus of
Charlotte Street, London, sell liquid yeasts from the Continent,
suitable for cool fermentation, to amateur winemakers.

Making white wine

There are specialist books on vinification both for the professional and
for the amateur. A list is given in Appendix 2. The basic method for
white wine is as follows:

PREPARATION

Having prepared the winery and the equipment, and with the starter yeast solution bubbling away, everything is given a final, thorough cleaning with sulphited water. The winery itself is washed down. The press, the crusher, the picking baskets and bins are all made as clean and sterile as possible.

PICKING

The grapes are picked into polythene baskets or containers, which are tipped into polythene bins and taken to the winery for processing immediately (unless they are being sent away, in which case they are carefully crated, loaded and transported as soon as possible to their destination).

CRUSHING AND PRESSING

The grapes are crushed, either in a grape crusher, or by being trampled with the feet or crushed with the hands, before being pressed. Pressing is done slowly and gently. When it seems that most of the juice has been extracted, the pulp is removed, taken out and returned to the press for a second pressing. Large modern horizontal presses do this job automatically. After the second pressing, this part of the process is complete.

SULPHITING

As the juice runs from the press it is collected in containers and is immediately sterilized by adding 1 g of sodium metabisulphite, or two Campden tablets, per gallon (4.5 litres) of juice. The sterilizing substance used is dissolved in a small quantity of the juice and then added to the container. The containers are then covered.

CHAPTALIZING

A sample of the juice is tested with a hydrometer for sugar content. Grape juice is denser than water because of the pulp debris suspended in it and also because it contains sugar. So measuring how much more dense juice is than water gives an indication of how much sugar it contains. The relative density is measured with a hydrometer, which looks like a fishing float. The denser the liquid, the higher the hydrometer floats.

The graduations on hydrometers are numbered in various ways. Some give a direct reading of relative density (or 'specific gravity' as it used to be known). This is the ratio of the density of the juice being measured to the density of water at the same temperature. Many hydrometers used for measuring sugar content are calibrated in Oechsle degrees. To get from relative density to Oechsle degrees: subtract 1 and multiply by 1000. A relative density of 1.07 is 70 °Oe, a relative density of 1.14 is 140 °Oe.

A liquid is denser when cold than when warm. Most hydrometers are designed to be accurate when the temperature of the must is 20 °C, so a thermometer is used to find out the actual temperature of the must. Subtract 1 °Oe for every 5 °C below 20 °C. The debris floating in the must is also allowed for by subtracting 2 °Oe from the reading.

To take an example, the hydrometer is floated in the must and the liquid comes up to 70 on the scale. 2 °Oe are subtracted to allow for the debris, leaving 68 °Oe. The temperature of the must is 15 °C, so 1 °Oe is subtracted to allow for this. The sugar content is thus estimated to be 67 °Oe.

TABLE 3. Interpretation of Hydrometer Readings

Reading on hydrometer in must (°Oe)	Sugar content of must (grams per litre or pounds per hundred UK gallons)	Potential alcohol content (% by volume)
50	103	6.0
52	108	6.3
54	114	6.7
56	119	7.0
58	124	7.3
60	130	7.6
62	135	7.9
64	140	8.2
66	146	8.6
68	151	8.9
70	156	9.2
72	162	9.5
74	167	9.8
75	170	10.0
76	172	10.1
78	178	10.5
80	183	10.8
82	188	11.0
84	194	11.4
86	199	11.7

Table 3 can then be consulted to calculate how much sugar to add to the must to bring it up to the desired sugar content of between 75 °Oe and 85 °Oe, depending on how high an alcoholic content is desired. Table 3 is based on George Ordish's table in his *Vineyards in England and Wales*. It is convenient to have the sugar concentration in grams per litre as this figure is the same as that for kilograms per 1000 litres or (practically) pounds per 100 UK gallons. Thus the same table is useful for both small and large crops. It is also convenient to have the information to be able to work out the amount of sugar needed for any desired alcohol content.

Once the hydrometer reading has been taken, it is simple to calculate how much sugar to add to the must to bring it up to the desired sugar content. For example, if the natural density of the must is 68 °Oe, the table shows that it already contains 151 grams of sugar per litre. If the winemaker wishes to bring it up to 80 °Oe, he must add enough to increase the sugar content to 183 grams per litre. 151 subtracted from 183 leaves 32, so the winemaker must add 32 grams of sugar per litre of must. Or, he can add 32 lb of sugar per 100 gallons of must. The sugar is stirred into the must until it has dissolved.

ACIDITY

The next job is to test for acidity. Many shops sell acid-testing kits and more accurate apparatus and chemicals for testing acidity by titration are available from specialist firms (see Appendix 3). Acidity should not be higher than 0.65 per cent. If over this figure, it is reduced by adding small amounts of precipitated chalk. 3.0 grams of chalk per gallon reduce acidity by 0.1 per cent. It is unlikely that acidity will be over 0.88 per cent and if this occurs frequently, it indicates that the wrong vine variety is being grown. To correct high acidity, water can be added as a last resort, although this practice is frowned upon as it dilutes an already poor wine.

FIRST RACKING

Now that the must has been sterilized and the sugar content and the acid content have been adjusted, the must is covered and left to settle for two days, to allow dirt and debris to sink to the bottom. It is then siphoned into clean fermentation containers, carefully, to avoid disturbing the sediment. For the start of the ferment the must should, ideally, be at a temperature of 18–21 °C (64–70 °F).

The weather is often chilly at this time of year and some artificial heat may well be necessary in the winery to warm up the must before the yeast starter is added and the ferment has begun. After adding yeast, airlocks are fitted to the containers. People who are accustomed to making country wines may be taken aback to find that the ferment does not immediately begin to bubble away. It may take up to a week for fermentation to begin, because of the inhibiting presence of sulphur dioxide. If nothing has happened after a week, it probably means that the sulphiting was overdone. Re-racking into fresh containers, which aerates the must, is the treatment and after this there should be no more trouble.

FERMENTATION

A slow, steady, cool fermentation is the aim. The liquid yeasts, which are available from Loftus, perform well at low temperatures so, once fermentation has begun, the temperature of the winery should be allowed to drop to between 13 and 16 °C (55–61 °F). Remember that the fermenting must itself gives off heat.

Sometimes it is far from obvious that fermentation is proceeding and a hydrometer should be used to make sure that all the sugar has been converted into alcohol. Once a relative density (specific gravity) reading of 0.990 has been taken, fermentation is at an end. It generally takes about three weeks.

RACKING

Once fermentation is complete, the wine is left to settle for a limited time, which should never exceed six weeks, and is then carefully racked into clean containers, leaving a sediment of dead yeast behind. This sediment will ruin the wine if racking is delayed for more than six weeks after the end of fermentation.

STABILIZATION

Airlocks and clean stoppers are fitted to the new containers, which should be quite full to prevent the air spoiling the wine.

ADJUSTING THE SULPHUR DIOXIDE LEVEL

Most of the SO_2 which was added to the must will have been used up by now, and the wine should be protected by adjusting the free sulphur dioxide level to 50 milligrams per litre. The SO_2 content is measured by means of a sulphur dioxide measuring cylinder, which is filled with wine up to the bottom of the scale on the side of the cylinder. Tiny amounts of 'blue solution' are added from a glass pipette. After each addition, the cylinder is shaken up, care being taken to avoid spilling any of the liquid, and the blue colour will disappear. As soon as the blue colour persists in the liquid, the new level in the cylinder is noted on the scale and this will give the amount of free SO_2 present in the wine in milligrams per litre.

To adjust the free SO_2, calculate the number of litres of wine to be treated (1 gallon = 4.546 litres). Subtract the present free SO_2 content of the wine from the desirable 50 milligrams per litre. Multiply the result by the number of litres of wine to be treated and you will know the exact amount of SO_2 to be added.

Unfortunately, the chemical used will not be 100 per cent sulphur dioxide, so a further calculation is necessary. Sodium metabisulphite, the best form of SO_2 at this stage, contains 60 per cent sulphur dioxide so you must multiply the figure of the required SO_2 by 100 and divide by 60 to discover the exact amount of sodium metabisulphite to be added. (A small calculating machine is a great boon when doing these and other sums!)

TARTRATE CRYSTALS

For the next few weeks a cold winery is a great advantage, as low temperatures help to stabilize and clarify the wine, which will not freeze as long as the temperature is above $-4\,°C$ ($25\,°F$). One West Country grower told me that, during the blizzards of 1978, the snow blew into his winery and piled in deep drifts around the vats and yet no harm was done. Small quantities of wine are, of course, more vulnerable to extreme cold. Tartrate crystals, which are tasteless but disagreeable, form and sink in low temperatures, but disappear once the weather warms up again. The wine should be racked while still cold, before the crystals have the chance to dissolve, only to reappear at awkward moments.

FINING

A haze may well appear in the wine due to minute particles far too small to filter out; these particles will not settle as they are electro-statically charged and therefore repel each other.

If these particles are proteins, they are positively charged. They can be removed by using bentonite, which is negatively charged. The two sets of particles attract each other and sink to the bottom. Exactly the right amount of bentonite, no more, no less, should be used. To find out how much to use, dissolve 1 gram of bentonite in 100 millilitres of water. It may take an hour or two to dissolve – give it an occasional good shake. Measure four 50 millilitre samples of wine into four glass bottles, labelled 2, 3, 4 and 5. Shake up the bentonite solution and, using a graduated 5 ml pipette, add 2 ml of bentonite solution to the first sample, 3 ml to the second, 4 ml to the third and 5 ml to the last. Stir up the samples and leave for two days. Then take four test tubes, mark them so that you know which is which, and use a pipette to put some of the cleared portion of each sample into a test tube. Heat some water in a saucepan to 21 °C (70 °F), immerse the samples and keep the temperature steady at 21 °C (70 °F) for 15 minutes. The wine in the test tube which has the lowest dose of bentonite and has remained clear contains the correct dose. The number of millilitres of bentonite solution in that dose is the same as the number of grams of bentonite to be added to each gallon of wine.

The necessary amount of bentonite is measured out and added to ten times its weight of wine. This mixture is allowed to stand an hour or two and beaten vigorously from time to time to dissolve the bentonite. This solution is then thoroughly stirred into the bulk of the wine, which is then left to settle for about ten days before being racked off the light, fluffy sediment, which should not be disturbed.

TANNIN

Hazes may also be due to excess tannin which cannot be removed by bentonite, as tannin particles, like bentonite, are negatively charged. Gelatine will remove the haze but may also remove too much of the tannin. If the wine tastes about right before treatment, *equal* quantities of tannic acid and gelatine are added, but if the untreated wine has a harsh, tannin taste, the proportion of tannic acid to gelatine is reduced to between 50 and 75 per cent. Gelatine is only needed if bentonite has failed to clear the wine, or if the tannin taste is harsh and strong.

A 1 per cent solution of tannic acid and a 1 per cent solution of gelatine are made up by dissolving 1 gram of each in 100 ml of water. Samples of wine are put in labelled containers and the test proceeds exactly as for bentonite, with 2, 3, 4 and 5 ml of gelatine solution plus an equal quantity of tannic acid solution being added to the samples. However, for this test no heating is necessary. The sample which clears with the lowest dose of gelatine has the correct dose. The amount of tannic acid to be added can only be assessed by test-treating and tasting small samples of the wine. After the wine has settled for a few days, it is racked again off the sediment.

SWEETENING

As fermentation converts the sugar in the wine to alcohol, most wines are naturally dry, but can be sweetened before bottling. If this is done, it is essential to see that no fermentation occurs in the bottle. The best way to prevent this is to filter the wine, to get rid of any yeast cells, before bottling into bottles sterilized by a metabisulphite solution. Equipment for filtering and sterilizing can be hired. For small quantities a small filter of a type available to amateurs can be used. The filter sheets must be fine enough to do the job and time should be allowed for the wine to flow through without undue pressure being used. All bottling and filtering equipment should be sterilized before use.

The winery should be thoroughly cleaned before bottling takes place. Proper wine bottles, which need not be new, are the only bottles which should be used; Moselle or Hock bottles look best for white wine, as, unfortunately, there is no distinctive English bottle. Corks must always be new and of good quality.

The bottles are cleaned and then sterilized before use with a sulphur dioxide solution (30 g of sodium metabisulphite per litre of water or 5 oz per gallon). The corks are washed in several changes of warm water and then sterilized by being soaked in a rather weaker SO_2 solution than that used for the bottles (25 g of sodium metabisulphite per litre, or $3\frac{3}{4}$ oz per gallon). The corks tend to shoot out of the solution, so they must be weighed down to submerge them completely.

At least two people are needed for bottling and it is useful to have three people, one filling bottles, one corking and one sterilizing the next batch of bottles and clearing away those that have been filled.

STORING

Wine bottles are stored on their sides so that the cork cannot dry out and allow in the air or impurities. Temperature changes are bad for wine, so the storage area should be well insulated and kept, if possible, at a temperature of around 10–13 °C (50–55 °F).

White table wine produced in Britain should not be kept too long before being drunk. It will usually be ready after a year, and should not generally be kept more than four or five years. Different wines vary in this respect and some growers have found certain wine varieties give wine which matures rather slowly (see pages 23–30 for information on vine varieties).

Red wine

Red wine is made from black grapes and the colour comes from the skins.

The grapes are destalked and then crushed. Sulphur dioxide is added to the pulp in the way already described for white wine and a sample of juice is taken. The sample is tested for sugar and acid content and adjustments are made, as for white wine. Starter yeast is added and the fermenting pulp is left in a vat or bin and turned twice a day until the desired degree of colour is reached, probably after about three days. While this first fermentation is taking place, the bin is kept covered with muslin and thick blankets to keep out insects and infections. The fermenting pulp is then pressed and the juice put into a clean cask or carboy. Fermentation then proceeds as for white wine.

Unfortunately, it is most unlikely that a red wine made from grapes grown in the British Isles will taste good. Most people prefer to make white wine and buy their red wine from sunnier countries, and on the evidence of the English red wines I have tasted so far, I feel that they are right, but see page 30 for red wines made from Zweigeltrebe grapes.

Rosé is made in the same way as red wine, but a proportion of white grapes can be used and the wine is not left so long on the skins.

CHAPTER ELEVEN

✿ *The French Way*

If one shut one's eyes, thought of wine, and named the first country that came to mind, it would probably be France. No nation produces a greater variety of wines than France, and, more to the point, no people consume more wine than the French. Wine in France is the standard drink, more common on the table than water, cheaper (if it's *ordinaire*) than fizzy lemonade. When it is so cheap and plentiful, some people still make it at home for the sake of having something special; the similarities of their experience to ours seem more important than the differences, and I feel that many growers may be interested to investigate what goes on over the Channel.

The world's biggest vineyard is the Midi, from the Rhône west to the Pyrenees, from the Massif Central south to the Mediterranean coast. For the last one hundred years, wine grapes have been far and away the major crop there – the rolling countryside is covered in vineyards: small, family-held plots that intersect like the pieces of a jigsaw puzzle, between the walled towns of pale stone and Roman-tiled roofs, at the feet of the low, stony mountains. Almost every village has its *cave coopérative* (community winery), where each farmer adds his harvest to the rest. Thus, making wine at home has been almost abandoned there, whereas at one time it was a major occupation; the fine old wine presses and oak casks stand idle.

At least two farmers still make wine for the family at home. One, Vincent Thierry, is a commercial vintner, who sends most of his crop to the *cave coopérative* and grows his grapes on a large commercial scale using the cooperative's resources but reserves two hundred of the best *souches* (vine plants) to press at home for a fine wine for private consumption. The other, Florian Geiger, is a former architect from Munich who now lives on an almost self-sufficient little farm up a dirt track, without electricity or plumbing, dedicated to ecological soundness and harmony with nature. Yet both use almost identical techniques and equipment in making wine – differing little from the method employed generally by everybody in the Midi a century ago. Geiger's grapes are Bourrais blanc, a hardy variety that resists the weather well and doesn't suffer too drastically if pruning or harvesting is late. Thierry uses three kinds of white grapes in equal parts: Macabel, Cervent and Muscat. Both Geiger and Thierry make dry, fresh, aromatic white wine – 'natural and frank' said Thierry. His neighbours agree.

To prepare the *souches* for bearing grapes, they must be skilfully pruned. A badly pruned *souche* will take years to recover, so the operation requires especial care and exactness, though each *souche* takes only a minute to prune. Pruning can be done any time during the winter. It should be completed no later than March so that the *souche* has time to recover from the shock of being cut before the start of the growing season in April. (The old branches, *sarments*, make a particularly fragrant fire: meat, especially lamb, grilled over *sarments* is a regional speciality.) The object of pruning, of course, is that the *souche* should be healthy and symmetrically balanced. So one chooses the four hardiest branches on either side of the *souche* and prunes them back to the point where there are two buds at the end of each: sixteen buds in all, eight on either side. More buds than that would require too much energy for the *souche* to maintain all the branches. When he was inexperienced, Geiger once tried cutting some *souches* back to where they had only eight buds in total; he ended up with eight thick, fat, soft branches that were easily bent and broken by the wind.

The Midi is ideally favoured with sun (plenty of it) and rain (enough so that the farmer need not irrigate) for the growing of wine grapes. The single feature of the weather that imperils the plant is the wind. Besides the infamous mistral, there are two dozen other winds that sweep over the countryside. For this reason, the *souches* are grown low; the plant is kept to little more than one metre high. Before the branches have started to grow, Geiger, who does not use posts and wires, must tie the plant to the stake on the side away from the prevailing wind so the *souche* can lean against it. From the woods near his farm, Geiger cuts chestnut stakes, half a metre high, for the purpose. To ensure that the stakes will resist moisture, he chars them in the fire before they are used.

The stake needs to be as close to the *souche* as possible without damaging the roots. Stakes must be replaced if they rot, and moved if they start restricting the development of the *souche*. Cloth ties tend to cut the wood; broad strips of flexible plastic are better. Geiger gets scraps for nothing from a local anorak factory.

Thierry employs another method, more time-consuming and expensive but more effective, too, because it steadies the plants better against the wind. It's a method used a lot in Italy, where the *souches* can reach heights of up to 3 metres (10 feet), like little trees. Wire is strung from iron stakes, and then a single long branch from each *souche* is bound with plastic to the wire; thus when pruning, one branch must be left long. In the South of France a trellis is not usually used, just a stake for each plant with the branches left loose.

Soil in the South of France is hard and stony, rather like baked clay. Fertilizer is applied. Geiger uses animal manure and plants clover to replenish nitrogen. He also uses an organic phosphorus compound; 300 g (10 oz) of fertilizer are sprinkled alongside each *souche*, to be washed into the soil by the rain, once a year in winter.

Apart from manuring, which he does every three years in the manner described above, Thierry mixes a foliar feed with fungicide and applies both together. The chief enemies of the vine in this region are oidium, a disease that attacks both leaf and grape and is eliminated with sulphur, and downy mildew, which comes with the rain and is attacked with copper sulphate. Geiger, though he is committed to organic farming, found he couldn't do without these fungicides. He sprinkles sulphur powder regularly and sprays copper sulphate mixed with water twice, before a big rain if possible (one tries to estimate the time and apply the copper sulphate as late as possible without being too late). In his potato patch, Geiger has successfully kept disease down with *prèle* (horse-tail), which grows abundantly by river banks: it's dried, then covered with water and cooked for an hour, and then the liquid is strained off and sprayed as a pesticide, but he hasn't yet tried it on the grapes. Geiger doesn't bother with insecticides; he feels that they do more harm than insects.

While the grapes are sweetening on the vine, the press and the casks must be prepared to receive them. In this region, everybody used to make wine at one time and so the traditional equipment, new one hundred years ago, is still about.

The wine press has a circular, cast-iron base, supported on a tripod or on wheels. A big steel screw is fixed through the centre, with a heavy top and a long cast-iron handle. A grille, the horizontal bars iron and the vertical bars oak, is fitted over the plate. Geiger's press measures about 1.5 m (5 feet) in diameter and its height is about 2 m (6 feet

6 inches). He's been borrowing it for the past eight years from a local farmer; the farmer always imagines he may use it one day, but never has got around to it so far, so the press remains on Geiger's farm. Thierry's press is identical in form but smaller.

Casks, too, survive, built of oak with iron bands. If prevented from getting mouldy, a cask ought to last at least fifty years, becoming hard, fragrant and deep red inside. There are plenty of old casks around, but new casks are still made by local artisans; one holding 100 litres (22 gallons) of wine will cost 100 francs (about £12).

The press is cleaned, simply with water, just before it's used. Casks, of course, since they have longer contact with organic matter, require more thorough cleaning as soon as they're emptied, and then again before they're refilled. When a cask has been emptied, Geiger first rinses it immediately. He next fills it with 4 litres (7 pints) of boiling water mixed with a handful of soda (for a 100 litre [22 gallon] cask). A heavy chain is lowered through the hole attached to a thin wire which protrudes a little when the cask is corked (so that the chain doesn't fall in). The chain acts as a scrubbing brush. The corked cask must be rolled vigorously about so that every surface is cleaned. It gets another rinse of plain cold water. Then a small plate of sulphur, suspended through the hole on a thin wire, is burned for a final disinfecting. Little holes and cracks can be repaired with mastic gum. Just before the refilling of the casks, each is examined (by means of the nose) and rinsed again. If it has recently been disinfected with sulphur, this step may be omitted, but in general it is wise to ensure that there are no fungi in a cask about to receive new wine.

The cellar must be made ready, too. In France, people do not have underground cellars – the cellar, or *cave*, is at ground level. In the old days, besides housing wine casks, the *cave* was where a few domestic animals might live; nowadays people keep their motor bikes in the *cave*. Geiger, whose farm consists of several small buildings, has the *cave* under his workshop. Its walls are old stone, its floor is earth and the low ceiling, which he built, is wood (with the concrete floor of the workshop above it). Wooden racks, about 1 m (3 feet) in height, support the wine casks along the walls, a larger wicker basket or two holds clean bottles, and there's a shelf for repair supplies, corks and cheesecloth. Geiger makes sure that all the casks are well balanced. Then he wheels the heavy press to the *cave* door (it's too big to go inside the doorway), so that he can give his full attention to the winemaking, with everything set for use.

Home harvesting in the Midi generally takes place directly after the commercial harvest, for the simple reason that all the resources of the community are mobilized for the commercial harvest and it's hard to find a spare bucket or a friend to help while that is going on. Both Thierry and Geiger generally harvest their grapes in the middle of October. Thierry harvests only 200 *souches*, to make 150 litres (33 gallons) of fine wine (he gets the rest of his wine from the *cave coopérative*, as part of his share of the profits). His harvesting, with about ten friends to help, gets done in about half a day. Geiger, who makes all the wine his family will use, has 750 *souches* which yield about 500 litres (110 gallons) of wine. In 1977, it took five people a day to get the harvest in; the year before, fifteen came, but most of them were inexperienced and it was difficult to supervise so many. The ideal number, he says, would be ten: six cutters, two porters, two at the press. Geiger uses plastic buckets borrowed from a local vintner (making up with lightness what they lack aesthetically). Thierry uses his own old *comportes* of chestnut wood. No special tools are essential to cut the grapes – anything with a sharp blade will serve, and some of Geiger's friends used scissors. If the weather is wet (which means the harvesting must be done in a particular hurry), a hole can be cut in a large plastic sack, of the sort used for fertilizer or animal food, which can be tied around the waist to make a giant apron.

Geiger's porters carry wooden mallets, to press the grapes down in the buckets to get them as full as possible, before making the trip from vineyard to press. Thierry, however, wants his grapes intact until the moment they're crushed in the press, so that they don't start fermenting in the bucket.

As each bucket is emptied into Geiger's press, its contents are trampled down. When all the grapes are in the press, they are thoroughly trampled for an hour (two people take turns of half an hour each). He remembers a tall woman with long legs dyed in grape juice, moving in time to the drum (the rhythm makes it easier to carry on this strenuous task, which is rather like walking through a swamp). When the trampling is finished, three men are needed to lift on the lid and heavy screw top, which weighs 200 kg (4 cwt). A sieve is hung over the lip of the press, where the juice comes out, to trap large particles. Now the pressing begins, by moving the handle back and forth rapidly for the first three hours. After that, the juice has ceased to run out quickly, and the handle is given another single, gentle turn every fifteen minutes or so for about a day and a half, until finally no more liquid comes. (The press should never be forced; one advantage to a hand press is that it lacks the power to extract the bitter juice of the stems.) Next, Geiger unscrews the lid, climbs into the press and, with a billhook and spade, loosens the hard cake of stems, skins and still-intact grapes that have eluded the press and are embedded in the skins and stems. He shovels this mixture into buckets and then tosses it back into the press for a second crushing, which takes another half day and yields about 20 per cent more juice. Thierry follows the same procedure, omitting the trampling, but, since his press is small, the two completed pressings take a total of four hours; he fills the press with new grapes four or five times, so the job takes sixteen to twenty hours in all.

Neither winemaker adds sugar, though as a matter of course the sugar content of the juice is ascertained with a hydrometer. Geiger has found that even juice with 6 per cent potential alcoholic content makes perfectly good wine.

Thierry ferments his wine in open vats of oak wood. For the first two weeks of intense fermentation, they're left completely uncovered. Then, as fermentation slows and the wine cools, a lid is laid on lightly. After a month, the process is finished and the wine should be transferred to sealed casks, but if Thierry can't get to the task immediately, he screws the lid tightly on each vat to keep the air off.

Geiger owns no vats; his wine is fermented in casks, in keeping with his principle of making multiple use of minimal equipment. Ten litres (2 gallons) at a time, buckets of juice are poured into each cask through a funnel, which also contains a cheesecloth filter. When a cask is full, he attaches a thin piece of cheesecloth over the hole, to keep vinegar flies from getting in while allowing fermentation gases out. The casks can't be completely filled, or they'll start foaming. Geiger determines when fermentation is over by listening; when it's finished, the hissing stops. Autumn temperatures in the Midi are generally suitable for fermentation (10 °C, 50 °F). Only once was it necessary to protect the wine from cold, when frost came early. Geiger draped the casks in old blankets so the process wouldn't stop too soon.

At the end of fermentation, the wine must be siphoned into the new container. A narrow, flexible, rubber tube, about 2 m (6 feet 6 inches) long, is fixed along a stick; the end of the stick protrudes 50 mm (2 inches) beyond the end of the tube. Then, when stick and tube are inserted in the cask (or vat), the stick will touch the bottom but the tube will be held above the layer of sediment which is left behind. (The sediment is used afterwards as compost, or for rendering clay walls.)

Next, the wine must be placed in sealed casks to age, filled to the top this time. Oak casks are ideal. Geiger uses the same ones in which the wine fermented, after rinsing them thoroughly in cold water. He fills them by means of a rotating system, transferring wine from a fermentation cask to a fresh one, then washing out the fermentation cask and siphoning wine from the next cask to the washed one, and so on. Geiger has found that pouring a layer of olive oil into the cask at the end (about a cupful in 100 litre casks) will retard evaporation. Of course, the oil doesn't mix with the wine, but it may impart a very slight flavour, so he intends to experiment with tasteless paraffin oil next time.

The wine should remain in the cask for at least a year. At the end of this time, Thierry transfers his into 80 litre (18 gallon) casks and leaves it for another two years. Then he attaches a tap to the cask and enjoys the fruits of his labours. He doesn't bottle the wine he makes for home use, but simply fills pitchers for the table as needed. He finds it keeps well for several months after the cask has been broached. He likes his wine best when it's three years old, but he's kept some in casks for as long as ten years; it's still quite drinkable but too sour for his taste by then.

Because Geiger's supply of casks is limited, he must bottle his wine before each harvest. In fact, he tends to start bottling it earlier than that, by July, because summers are very hot and he doesn't trust his cellars to stay cool enough to ensure that the wine won't start fermenting again. He is able to collect bottles from cafés and from friends, so he never needs to buy them, but sometimes he will do so when he wants to give a few bottles away as gifts. Used bottles can be cleaned with warm soda water (not too hot, or the bottle will break) and a bottle brush. Corks cost 10 centimes each, but to avoid that expense, they can be made out of ordinary wood wrapped in cheesecloth. Geiger uses chestnut. If he's going to give a bottle away, instead of labelling it, Geiger 'makes his etiquette', as the French say, by lightly spattering the bottle with a mixture of water and the scarlet, iron-rich earth of the hills around his farm. The oldest bottle of his wine that Geiger has tasted was three years old, and he says it was the best, but usually the family consumes everything by the end of each year. Some bottles have travelled as far as Germany, and they apparently survived the journey well. Thierry's wine has never been far from home, no farther than a family picnicking spot.

If the secateurs are kept sharpened and the vats, casks and press properly cleaned, the only expense for these winemakers is fertilizer and fungicide (plus a few bottles and corks for Geiger). Labour is the chief cost. The reward: the pleasure of accomplishment and a wine of personal character, like no other.

London: *English wine in the Mall*

Tradition in England—technology in Europe.
English estate-bottled wine
has to compete with the cheaper wines,
siphoned from the European wine lake

Charles Clive-Ponsonby-Fane enjoying a glass of his own wine, Brympton d'Evercy

Italian wine being pumped ashore in France

(OPPOSITE ABOVE) Pickers at New Hall Vineyard in Essex
(OPPOSITE BELOW) Franciscan friars helped to pick the 1964 harvest at Beaulieu Abbey, where Cistercian monks had planted a vineyard seven hundred years before

The new vineyards are widely distributed, from Jersey in the south to Derbyshire in the north, and from East Anglia to the west of Ireland

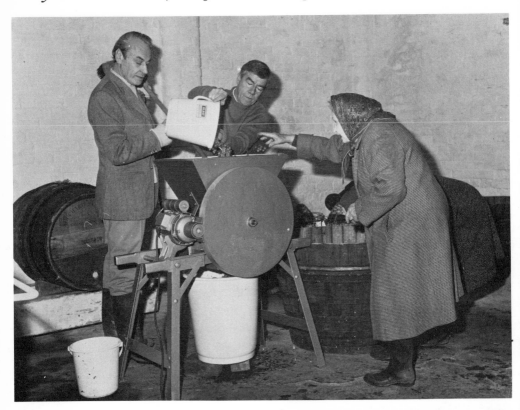

(ABOVE) Alan Rook (*left*) with his mother and a friend, making wine at Stragglethorpe, Lincolnshire. This was Europe's most northerly vineyard until Reresby Sitwell planted his at Renishaw in Derbyshire
(RIGHT) Robin Don (*left*) has a fruitful vineyard at Elmham Park in Norfolk

(OPPOSITE) George Ordish harvesting grapes with his wife and children. From three sides of a small house and quarter of an acre of garden, Mr Ordish produced a bottle of wine for every day of the year

Vines in the open and under glass

Vine arch at Powis Castle, Wales

Grapes under cloches at the Oxted
Viticultural Station

The Great Vine at Hampton Court, two hundred years old; its main branch is over a hundred
feet long

Preparing and improving the soil

Digging a trench for vines in a garden

These vines at Westbury were planted in unploughed grassland which had been treated with Gramoxone

The Merrydown Wine Company's vineyard at Horam, Sussex, is on heavy clay improved by drainage and massive applications of compost

Vine varieties and rootstocks

Madeleine Angevine

Seibel

Scheurebe

The grateful French erected this monument to Jules Planchon, who grafted the European vine on to an American rootstock and thus saved the vineyards of Europe from extinction by phylloxera

Müller-Thurgau

Siegerrebe

Planting: the old and the new ways

Traditional methods: French peasants hoeing a vineyard

Modern methods: Geneva Double Curtain, developed for mechanical harvesting

Bamboos for staking can be grown in the garden. This photograph was taken in Cornwall, c. 1900

Typical modern Double Guyot system, wide planting

Using a crowbar to make holes for stakes

Vines planted in black polythene to keep down weeds and conserve warmth and moisture

(OPPOSITE) Sir Guy Salisbury-Jones at Hambledon, where his vines are grown low in the French way

Pruning and training

The Max Tapener Gun speeds the work of tying in the vines

Pruning in early spring

Clipping back the shoots in the summer once the top wire has been reached

Vine flowers

Summer pruning. Leaves are removed from around the forming fruit to give light and air

Tucking in the growing shoots

Tying in new growth

Climate, pests and diseases afflict British and Continental vines

Problems arise where vines are virtually the only crop, as here in the Champagne district

A French viticulturist sets off a rocket to precipitate a hailstorm before it can damage the crop

Netting is the most effective protection against birds

Spraying by tractor at Wootton Vines

Sprays have been used for a long time. A Victorian version of the knapsack sprayer, note the ingenious overhead pumping device

Know your enemies

Oidium (powdery mildew)

The *pourriture noble* (noble rot)

Plasmopara (downy mildew)

Botrytis which, in the form of the 'noble rot', can concentrate the sugar in the grapes under certain weather conditions; more usually it rots the grapes and severely reduces the crop

Phomopsis (dead arm)

Harvesting and winemaking

The harvest at Hambledon

Checking the sugar content of the fruit

Sir Guy Salisbury-Jones testing the grape juice for sugar content

A grape transporter at Three Choirs Vineyard

Trampling grapes before pressing

Pressing the grapes

A home made wine press, using a car jack to apply pressure

Wine press on its trolley

Modern grape crusher, Hambledon

Modern wine press, Wootton Vines

Wine press at Three Choirs Vineyard,
Gloucestershire; this is one of the vineyards
which will make wine for other growers

After the pressing, the skins, stalks and debris
are discarded

Straining the must into carboys

Amateur winemaker's equipment

The winery at Westbury has modern fermentation vats for large quantities and glass carboys for small amounts

Filling a pipette by suction

A finger over the top of the pipette will stop the juice running out

Sterilizing bottles for use

Filling the bottles

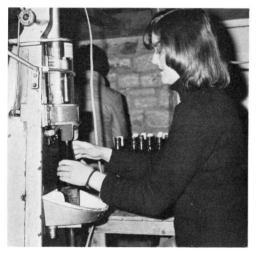
Corking by machine

Capping the bottles

Wine in the cellar

Storing on shelves

Cases of Penshurst 1977

The French way

The Midi: burning vine prunings

Straining the juice through a basket

French harvesters

Wooden mallet, used to press down the grapes
(OPPOSITE) The Cave co-operative where
most of the wine is made

Michael Waterfield in his vineyard, Marriage Hill, high up in the Downs near Wye, in Kent

Manager Bill Carcary weighs the grapes at
Hambledon

Bernard Theobald of Westbury

Pamela Smith assesses the crop at Flexerne

Dr Idris Thomas of Wern Dêg in Wales

Marketing the wine

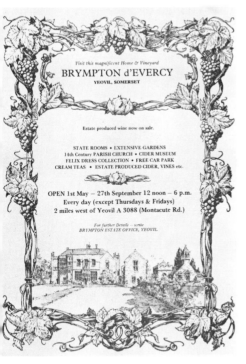

Brympton d'Evercy's enticing poster

The ideal outlet: Michael Waterfield's restaurant at Wye

Hoe Vineyard's wine is used entirely for making mustard

Mr Ambrose of Cavendish Manor, photographed for the local newspaper

The vine, brought by the Romans, flourished in England throughout the Middle Ages and survived until the First World War

William the Conqueror, uncertain of the native vintage, brought his own wine in 1066. The Bayeux Tapestry shows wine casks being taken to the ships

A fifteenth century harvest from the *Kalendar of Shepherds*, a book popular in France and in England for two hundred years (Paris 1493)

Welsh vendange, at Castell Coch, in the nineteenth century

Beaufoy's Wine Manufacturing at Lambeth was making large quantities of white wine in 1791, but the grapes were probably imported. Henry Beaufoy grew grapes in Lambeth under glass and delighted in sending bunches to his friends

The vineyard at Castell Coch

The long tradition

A medieval wine press (B.M. Cotton Ms.)

Beer replaced wine, but the vine was not forgotten

Lord Bute, pioneer of Welsh vineyards, in 1872

Wine press at Cardiff Castle, where Lord Bute's wines were made

Revival

Ray Barrington Brock, whose researches helped to revive the English vineyards

Making wine at Edward Hyams' vineyard in 1954

Edward Hyams in 1949

Recognition

(ABOVE) The vineyards of the United Kingdom

(LEFT) Recognition came at last in 1979, when Mr Jack Ward, Chairman of the English Vineyards Association and of the Merrydown Wine Company, was awarded the O.B.E. for his services to the English wine industry

CHAPTER TWELVE

🌺 Marketing English Wines

The growth rate in the consumption of all wines in Britain is amongst the highest in Europe. Thus, those bringing their wine to the market, for the next few years at least, will find marketing conditions favourable and the problems only those common to all marketing. The marketing of English wines should therefore be the easiest part of the whole cycle. There are no wine lakes in Britain and there are not likely to be for many years to come, provided that British growers concentrate on high-quality wine. The grower of such wines may even be reluctant to sell them, unlikely though this seems. Replacements are slow to come by and while fine wines stay in the cellar, they appreciate in value or, at the very least, keep pace with inflation. Antiquarian book dealers, for example, have the same problem.

The small grower, producing for himself and his family, has no trouble with marketing his wine. He simply stores it and drinks it with his family and his friends. So long as none of it is for sale, then he pays no tax and the Customs and Excise will not trouble him. If he and his family and friends drink two bottles a day his saving for a year is £1460 at current prices according to a calculation made by Mr Jack Ward. Depending on his level of income tax, the figure in terms of pre-tax salary is very much higher. If wine drinkers costed out their purchases accurately for a year, they might be astonished at the amount spent and thus the amount which might be saved by growing their own.

If the grower wishes to sell his wine, however, his first step must be to register with the Customs and Excise. He should also consult experts on income tax about allowable costs, the cost of marketing of course being one.

Thus it is difficult to drift into selling and it is sensible to devise a marketing policy which will aim to sell the wine at the right time at a price which brings the maximum profit for a minimum cost. In other words, ideally, the growers want to be able to dictate marketing terms and enjoy a true sellers' market. Mr Barnes of Little Whatmans, Biddenden, Kent, told the 1978 EVA wine conference that what started him growing vines was his feeling of helplessness as an apple producer. He harvested his crop, sent it to the London market and had no control over the price it fetched. Often he found that he was selling at a loss. He deliberately looked for an agricultural business in which he had control of the whole operation. He has found that vine-growing answers his need so well that he has gradually increased to 6.5 ha (16 acres) under vines.

The most profitable way of marketing wine, if it works, is to sell it at the vineyard gate and use no other distribution channel. The full sales revenue is retained and clerical, packing and freight charges are nil. However, if sales are too slow, then outlets in the wine trade or in other trades can be found. A retailer needs attractive packaging for his shop displays, reasonable credit terms and a buying price which allows him to make a profit comparable to that made on his other lines. Once a retailer is committed to selling your wine the most important thing remaining is to ensure continuity of supply.

Continuity is vital. There is no profit in persuading people to stock your wine who, in their turn, work at establishing regular customers for your product only to spoil everything by irregular supplies. Continuity does not necessarily mean that the customer can have all he wants, when he wants. There may have to be a rationing system – so many bottles per month. Or, there might be an annual stock sale, much as Beaujolais is handled, and wine released at one given point in the year. It all depends on production and cash-flow requirements and, of course, on how thirsty customers are for your product.

Marketing should, but often does not, start with the market and the first question to ask is what does the market want. The Barretts at Felsted have found that a white wine rather sweeter than suits their own palate is most in demand and many other producers are of this opinion. Thus, in planting policy and in the winery, a sweet product may be desirable, at present at any rate. Many growers regret this as the natural English wine has a sharp green freshness which is attractive and not easily found in imported foreign wines. It would seem that there is room for both sweet and dry English wines, though certainly the customers' preferences should not be ignored.

The market would obviously welcome an English red wine and there are rich rewards awaiting the first successful British vineyards to produce one. So far efforts in this direction have been mainly experimental and largely unsuccessful. An NFU spokesman said cautiously of Bernard Theobald's red wine, drunk at a 1978 Taste of England dinner, 'Well, it's young, red and undoubtedly English.'

The packaging of the wine is the next thing to think of. The temptation to save money here should probably be resisted. An attractive label and necklace on the bottle will go far to sell the wine and will be used for years, so it is important to get it right. Printing in four colours is desirable but is costly for a short run. At least two colours should be used. Emphasis on the place of origin generally helps sales, particularly if there are any local historic features of interest to be used on the label. Penshurst Vineyard has used a charming eighteenth century print of Penshurst but has incorporated a tiny kangaroo into the design as the proprietor is Australian. Wootton Vineyard was fortunate to find a medieval carving of grape stealers in nearby Winchester Cathedral. The help of a professional designer will save expensive errors. Printers who are experienced in wine-label work should be used, for labels which peel off in the cellar or turn musty quickly are a waste of money. Certain items of information must be given on labels in order to comply with EEC regulations, and this should be investigated before the label is printed. Up-to-date information can be obtained from the English Vineyards Association.

The bottle and the cork do not themselves allow much freedom of design, since choice has to be made from what is available. There are, however, powerful advocates of a distinctive English bottle, and this would command a great deal of support.

Extra sales can be made by packing in gift containers. The container should be brightly designed and have a built-in gift card; a three-bottle pack is attractive, and may contain three different wines. Consider ways of combining with other vineyards to bring down unit costs. The name of each vineyard could be overprinted on the pack. One argument for not blending some at least of the crop, is that more sales are made to people who buy 'one of each'. The gift pack can be general, or designed for Christmas, as a holiday souvenir, or any other specialized theme, such as a thousand years of the local church for example. This type of packaging is apt to be somewhat expensive, but a local firm could well be found which would give a reasonable price.

Having got the product and the packaging sorted out, the only thing left, before telling the world about the wine, is to decide the price. This is something which would obviously have been considered from the beginning.

You may be a vanity wine producer, like a vanity author – producing something because you want to, irrespective of cost and without hope of profit, but most growers hope to cover all costs of production and selling and still make a profit. However, it is no use pricing the wine out of the market and recovery of some costs may have to be spread over a period of years. English wine is at a disadvantage because of the present tax structure and because it has to bear vineyard establishment costs which Continental producers have long since forgotten. Its competitive advantage is that it is closer to the market, transport costs are lower and it is undoubtedly easy to sell. There is no reason, at present, at any rate, why English wine should be sold at any price other than at the maximum the market will bear. High prices are one way of ensuring continuity of supply. No producer should look at his neighbour's price and seek to undersell him. Special offers, discounts, and so on are just not necessary. The most that need be done is to give an occasional 'free' bottle for wine tastings.

With everything right, the grower can, with confidence, seek his market. He should supply his outlets and publicize his wines at the same time. Some retailers or wholesalers will be lively fellows, who will do their own shouting, but no risks should be taken. A local wine shop 'tried' a dozen bottles which remained at the back of the shop. They sold slowly and the shop manager refused to buy any more. He put down his failure to it being 'overpriced'. Had he and the supplier made a determined effort to sell them, the dozen would undoubtedly have been sold and a new outlet would have been established to the benefit of the English wine trade in general.

There is no end to the opportunities which will arise to publicize local wine. For some reason the press, radio and television are unusually keen to give free publicity to English wine – to an extent which would make other businesses very pleased indeed. (The cost of using advertising is relatively so high that it is unlikely to be profitable.) One new grower in Wales told me that the efforts of local television in offering news coverage was positively embarrassing and that if a crop was not produced soon, she would have to leave the district.

If the sales outlets are local, then local media should be approached. There might be a local correspondent who writes up the area events to contact, or possibly a hot line direct to the editor could be arranged. The picking of the grapes and work in the winery are attractive subjects for photography and television and, if editors are unable to spare a staff man, a local freelance photographer should be contacted.

If he is interested, he will do all the publicity work for the vineyard at no cost. But the moment publicity is really needed is when the year's vintage goes on sale for the first time.

This is the moment for a tasting, which can be held at home or the winery if it is suitable, but at any rate in a place with the right atmosphere. The wine should be in position some days beforehand and the 'staff', who may be only the rest of the family, should be at the tasting to answer questions. A simple, short press release, with the history of the vineyard and the basic statistics of production and price, should be available, together with a photograph of a bottle of wine and a list of stockists. Journalists usually enjoy tastings more if other people are there. Those invited might include suppliers (who can be relied upon to say the vineyard is thriving on their products) and customers, including managers, buyers and counter assistants, where big shops are involved, local hotel and restaurant managers and the local councillors who will support industry in the area by insisting on wines from their own district being available at council receptions. If radio or television are interested, they may well want an interview either in the vineyard or winery and time at the tasting should be allowed for this. Sound effects, such as the 'plop' of a cork being drawn or clinking of glasses, could be practised beforehand.

Sales may be made at the tasting, so be prepared for this by having someone there to take orders. Names and addresses of those attending should go into a visitors' book to form the basis of a direct mail list. Such lists, together with those taken at the vineyard gate, will form the basis of mailings in future years to announce new vintages.

Everything possible should be done to make a tasting a memorable success. Word-of-mouth advertising costs nothing, but it is often the most effective part of the marketing strategy. Everyone should leave the tasting convinced that the product is right, the price is right and knowing exactly where it can be bought. If sales are through retail outlets and hotels and restaurants, then they should all be on a list of stockists given to those who come to the tasting, and particularly to the press.

A successful wine-tasting party is a major hurdle passed. The main tasks now should be constant publicity of the wine and the vineyard, and support of stockists. Opportunities for continuing low-cost but still very effective publicity will be endless. 'Piggyback' publicity is particularly useful. An example of this would be to cooperate with a local motor-car dealer who is about to give a party to introduce a new

British car model to the district. If your wine is liked, customers might well be invited to a party to taste it and view the new model. Many hundreds of invitation cards will go out publicizing your wine at no cost to you. English wine has news value and this is helpful to the garage. British dealers in French cars used the 1978 *nouveau beaujolais* in this way.

Local fairs, bazaars and county shows will give opportunity for other piggyback arrangements. Alternatively, an exhibit of your own may be preferred. An attractive leaflet, with the story of the vineyard and how the wine is made, should be available. A robust stand could be constructed to serve for many such occasions. A model vineyard and winery could be constructed if skills allow. A leaflet of recipes using the wine and vine leaves, with gardening tips to promote the sale of cuttings, is simple and cheap to produce. Other products, such as books about wine and vineyards (including this one), can be stocked in cooperation with a local bookshop and sold both over the counter and by direct mail. All these things help to establish that English wine is here to stay – something very important to a long-term marketing scheme.

Continuing support of stockists is most important. Restaurants and hotels will use a small stand-up card on the table, saying 'Drink local wine' and mentioning the vineyard's name. If visitors are welcome, then leaflets can be left at reception desks with a map sketched in for the benefit of tourists. The sale price to the trade must be carefully worked out and a table for this is given in Appendix 8. The whole point of this structure is that the producing vineyard must never undersell the stockists, who must be able to compete on fair terms with each other.

If a stockist is big enough, it may be possible to organize an English wine week. If the stockist sells other English wines, so much the better. The real competition is not the vineyard down the road, but the foreigner.

Open days at the vineyard will greatly stimulate publicity and sales. All local societies should be circularized; they will come by the coach load, will sip glasses of wine whilst there and depart clutching bottles. Some producers have converted old farm buildings and serve meals of local foods with a glass of wine. One serves stuffed vine leaves. Here again, the emphasis is on quality; people coming for a day's outing want value for money but they will pay more, not less, to get it. Marketing on this scale needs careful financial control; car parks and lavatories have to be provided; kitchens have to be clean and efficient and a ready supply of staff available. It is, of course, possible to start with small occasional groups and build gradually.

The building used for visitors should be well decorated with photographs and press cuttings, labels, and so on, telling the story of English wine. The menu should reinforce the message; it should be attractively printed and tell the story of English wine. A small charge can be made for take-away souvenir menus. A sales point clearly recognizable as such for wines, books and vines should be strategically located. It should be possible for purchases to be made over the counter or whilst dining and added to the bill.

There are many vineyards now which have grown in order to serve existing outlets. Marriage Hill Vineyard, which supplies the Wife of Bath at Wye and Mr Kenneth Bell of Thornbury Castle restaurant, near Bristol, are two examples, and the famous restaurateur Robert Carrier is to plant a vineyard at Hintlesham Hall in Suffolk.

Some growers give lectures covering the story of English wine and how they are involved in it. This is an excellent method of publicity. Others enter their wines in competitions and win prizes and recognition. Some win export orders; some supply internationally famous hotels and restaurants and even the cruise liner *QE2* – all such orders being well publicized.

The important basic requirements in marketing wine are: get the product right, package it properly, price it correctly, both for the drinker and the stockist, leave the right margin for yourself, ensure continuity of supply and publicize it continually. These requirements are common to all marketing; the only difference is that marketing your own wine is a lot more fun.

CHAPTER THIRTEEN

✿ Case Histories

Breaky Bottom – Chilsdown – Cranmore – Felstar – Flexerne – An Foras Talúntais – Hambledon – Harefield – Longueville House – Marriage Hill – Maryville House – Penshurst – Pilton Manor – Renishaw Hall – Spots Farm – Wern Dêg – Westbury Farm – Wootton Vines

Breaky Bottom, RODMELL, EAST SUSSEX

MR PETER HALL

After taking a BSc degree, Peter Hall went into farming. He started work as an agricultural labourer to gain practical experience on the land, before becoming the tenant of a small farm on the Sussex Downs. He has renovated the farmhouse and the magnificent barn, which is now used for concerts and opera and is also his winery. He began as a pig farmer. Now the pigs have gone and have been replaced by sheep, but it is the vineyard which is Mr Hall's chief interest. In 1974, 3 acres of vines were planted and a further $\frac{1}{2}$ acre in 1975.

Breaky Bottom is 45 m (150 feet) above sea level in a bowl of the South Downs, not far from Lewes. The soil is fairly deep loam over chalk, with good, natural drainage. Situated as it is in arable farmland, the vineyard has been affected more than once by hormone weed-killers used by neighbouring farmers.

Several varieties of vines are grown, chiefly Müller-Thurgau, Seyval Blanc and Reichensteiner, with small numbers of Pinot Noir, Riesling, Schönburger and Bacchus. Nearly all are on SO_4 rootstock. On this chalky soil, Reichensteiner and Seyval Blanc are the most successful varieties, cropping well and giving wine of a fine quality.

The vines are planted 1.5 m (5 feet) apart with 2.1 m (7 feet) between the rows to allow room for the tractor, which is 1.5 m (5 feet) wide. The vines are allowed to grow up to 1.8 m (6 feet) above the ground, for Mr Hall is convinced that in northern latitudes, vines need a large area of foliage. The double wires, hooked to the end posts, are moved up during the season as the vines grow, thus the work of tucking in the shoots is minimized. Artificial fertilizers and foliar feed are used every year; a dressing of farmyard manure is applied every third year.

Mr Hall originally used strips of fine-meshed netting 1 m (39 inches) wide to protect the grapes from bird damage. These have now been replaced by overhead netting, which he has found to be more efficient, easier to handle and, above all, very much cheaper. It has cost £700 to cover the entire 4 acres with good-quality overhead netting; the strip netting would have cost roughly twice as much.

Fungicides are sprayed every two weeks with a recently acquired Berthoud sprayer; the old sprayer was inefficient and, in spite of the poor harvest of 1978, Mr Hall felt that this further investment was essential. Weeds, which were at first a problem, are controlled by Gramoxone and simazine in early spring. Round-up, expensive to buy but economical to use in small amounts, is used for spot treatment of thistles and other perennial weeds.

The wine made at Breaky Bottom is of a high standard, for Mr Hall, who is half French, understands wine and is a perfectionist, sparing no pains in his pursuit of excellence. Five thousand bottles were produced in 1977, but the light crop of 1978 has been a disappointment.

The total cost of the vineyard and winery has been £20,000 including labour, ploughing, posts, wires, vines and equipment. The winery has been equipped as cheaply as possible; the wine press was third hand and most of the equipment was supplied second hand by H. E. Lunken & Co. of London, who have been very helpful to Breaky Bottom and other vineyards. Nevertheless, investment has been considerable and vines are a difficult crop; Mr Hall feels strongly that success will come only to those who have skill, knowledge and a dedicated interest in wine and in vines.

Chilsdown, SINGLETON, WEST SUSSEX

IAN AND ANDREW PAGET

Ian Paget left his executive job in the brewery business at the age of thirty-two. He and his brother Andrew determined to become their own masters and plant a vineyard on 13 acres in the Sussex Downs at Singleton, near Chichester. Ten thousand Müller-Thurgau vines were planted in 1972, 5000 Chardonnay and 4000 Reichensteiner in 1973. A further 1200 Müller-Thurgau rooted cuttings were planted in 1975. The early years, while the Pagets were waiting for their first crop, were quite a struggle financially, but now Chilsdown is one of the most successful of English commercial vineyards.

By 1976 the Pagets had been able to convert the disused Singleton railway station, which they had acquired in 1971, into a well equipped winery to deal with the heavy Chilsdown yield of between eight and nine thousand bottles per acre.

Andrew Paget took a postal course in winemaking, run by Anton Massel (see page 155) and found to his relief that the wine he made at Chilsdown was eminently satisfactory.

The entrance to the vineyard is through a picturesque, creeper-hung archway under the old railway embankment. There is a wooden bench on a bank where we sat comfortably in the sun, sipping a refreshing glass of Chilsdown and admiring the rows of vines in their gently sloping, south-facing vineyard, sheltered from the north by a belt of trees and by the surrounding hills. The soil is silt over chalk and was improved before planting by an application of spent mushroom compost at seventeen tons per acre.

The original vines were planted 1.08 m (3 feet 6 inches) apart with 1.8 m (6 feet) between the rows; this was found to be too close. More recent plantings have been 1.2 m (4 feet) apart, with 1.8 m (6 feet) between the rows, although the Pagets now feel that this is on the narrow side and that 2.1 m (7 feet) would have been preferable.

Of their vines, all have been successful except for the Chardonnay. These were difficult to establish; many failed to survive and the remainder have never cropped well. The Pagets have now decided to grub them out and replace them.

The vines were hand-hoed for the first three years; Ian Paget estimates that he hoed 37 miles a year. Now they use herbicides and are impressed by Round-up. 'It kills everything.' (NB: Monsanto, the makers, stress that Round-up is a systemic herbicide, which must not be allowed to touch the foliage of the vine or it will be drawn into the system of the plant and kill it.) Round-up treatment costs the Pagets £24 per acre.

Fertilizing is entirely through foliar feeding with Maxicrop, which is based on seaweed. It is sprayed on with fungicide and the whole combined operation takes five and a half hours. They use one gallon of Maxicrop to the acre.

In the open downland, birds are not too much of a problem. Chilsdown has never been netted or protected in any way except by dawn and dusk patrols with a gun. There is a rabbit fence around the perimeter of the vineyard.

The wine is made by Andrew Paget in the booking hall of the former railway station. He recommends H. E. Lunken & Co. of London as suppliers of winery equipment and tanks. Both Pagets believe that wine should be as natural as possible, keeping additions of sugar and other additives to a minimum. The wine is very clean, light and dry. Chilsdown's average yield is 20,000 bottles; in 1976 it produced 10 per cent of the total quantity of English wine, on just 1 per cent of the total vineyard area.

The brothers used to do all the work themselves, but they have recently taken on one man full-time; another was working with them for one month, while on a pre-release course from the RAF. At harvest time, fifteen regular pickers harvest four tons of grapes a day.

Chilsdown exported 10 per cent of its output in 1975. The Pagets were pleased with this, pointing out that the Germans only export 8.5 per cent of their total production. The wine went to Germany, the Republic of Ireland, and the USA. Now, due to the heavy demand in the home market, exports are not worthwhile and have been stopped.

The Pagets encourage visitors, taking round parties by arrangement and having regular visiting times for people to taste and buy the wine and walk round the vineyard. They sell up to 20 per cent of their wine at the gate, collecting the entire profit without having to pay a middleman.

Ian Paget calculated that they had spent £10,000 establishing the vineyard. This covers everything – including sprays, machinery, vines, and their tractor – but excluding their labour. The winery has cost them £35,000. They estimate their gross returns average £2800 per acre and are very confident of the future.

Ian Paget refuses to blame the government for lack of help. 'They didn't ask us to set up a vineyard.' He believes in self-reliance. If the soil, the site and the vines are right, and if the *vigneron* is prepared to work hard and intelligently, then the Pagets feel there is no reason why an English vineyard cannot be extremely profitable.

Cranmore Vineyard, ISLE OF WIGHT

NICK POULTER AND ROBERT GIBBONS

Cranmore Vineyard, near Yarmouth on the Isle of Wight, was started on a part-time basis in 1967. By 1975 Mr Poulter and Mr Gibbons were both able to give up their full-time jobs to devote themselves entirely to their vineyard.

Today they have 7 acres planted with 10,000 vines and intend to

extend to 10 acres in time. The vineyard slopes slightly to the south-
west, and is on very heavy Isle of Wight clay.

When we visited, in mid-October, Mr Poulter and Mr Gibbons were
engaged in the long and tedious work of laying lightweight perforated
plastic drainage tubes (about 100 mm [4 inches] diameter) down the
vineyard in an effort to relieve the waterlogging which occurs so easily
in such heavy soil, and which inhibits the performance of the vines.
Mole drains carry the water to the drainage tubes which are laid in
trenches and covered with 'beach'.

In 1975 Mr Poulter and Mr Gibbons bought black mesh netting and
two days were spent putting it up. A gale promptly blew the lot down,
tearing it in half. Happily the suppliers took it all back. However, birds
seem not to be a problem, because there are large quantities of wild
fruit in the area, so now there is no netting at all at Cranmore.

The vines are a mixture of vines on their own roots propagated at the
vineyard and grafted vines imported between 1972 and 1974 from
Germany; but it has been found that, on their clay soil, grafted vines
do not do as well as vines on their own roots. Vines on rootstocks are

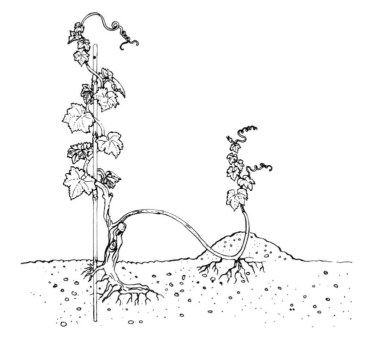

Converting a grafted vine to grow on its own roots, by layering

being taken back on to their own roots by layering; training down the scion canes to the ground and allowing them to root into the soil, which is piled up around them.

The soil is analysed every year by ADAS; this is felt to be essential. The foliar feed, Maxicrop, is used in addition to application of potash and phosphorus in autumn and nitrogen in spring.

Mr Poulter thinks leaf analysis is a very good idea in cases where vines show local deficiency symptoms.

Annual weeds, especially willow-herb, were rampant when we visited Cranmore vineyard and seedlings were to be dealt with using simazine and Gramoxone in spring. The vines are sprayed with sulphur, Elvaron and zineb; only £150 is spent each year on spraying, which Mr Poulter feels is very cheap considering the amount of wine produced. Cranmore uses a Berthoud sprayer which fits onto their small Ferrari tractor. Herbicides are usually applied with a knapsack sprayer. Self-heal (*Prunella vulgaris*) had been a problem in the past but was effectively eradicated using Round-up.

The vineyard is run entirely by Mr Poulter and Mr Gibbons, with help from the village only at harvest time.

Although Mr Poulter has written a short book on wine technology, *Wines from Your Vines*, he feels strongly that making wine is not learned by reading 'recipe' books but by experience. Good quality wine is 'grown' as well as 'made'. Fermentation takes place in fibreglass vats in a cellar building in the vineyard at approximately 10 °C (50 °F). The new grape press is in a cellar extension with a translucent roof. Mr Gibbons stresses that it is important to get the grapes from the vine to the press quickly for, if too long is taken, then oxidation occurs. They have a 300 litre (66 gallon) automatic press which is ample for their needs at present, but when they expand they will buy a second press of the same size rather than change their present one for a larger size. Thus, during bad weather, enough may be picked to fill the small press between showers, whereas a large press requires the certainty of longer dry spells in order to fill it.

Cranmore is often busier in winter than summer since Mr Gibbons and Mr Poulter do a large business in vines; they sell by mail order 60,000 to 80,000 vines per year, all propagated from cuttings at the vineyard nursery and sent out with a very detailed sheet of instructions for growing indoors or outside depending on the variety. For this they advertise to a certain extent in gardening magazines, but find that a lot of their business is done by word-of-mouth recommendation.

They have had their ups and downs; on one occasion they bought a load of sharp sand for potting some young plants and, to their horror, they found that the potting substance was contaminated with salt. The only vines which survived were those placed by a building where rain poured off the roof on to them. They can only guess that all this water washed the salt through and away from the plants. Mr Gibbons estimates that they lost about £500 through this. Despite such problems, the sale of vines is a very sound and profitable business, though a great amount of work is involved.

Cranmore used to supply amateur viticulturists with fungicides and fertilizers but, because of soaring postal charges, this has been discontinued.

They try to keep tourists to a minimum, except those who join their open-day tours, which are on Wednesday evenings in August and September. These tours are well arranged and in addition they have groups of ten or more by appointment at any mutually acceptable time. Casual visitors are most unwelcome as they make it difficult to continue the work of the vineyard. Because of their large mail order vine business, many people tend to turn up from all over Britain – quite unannounced – curious to see where their vines came from. For some strange reason, says Mr Poulter, people think vineyard owners have all the time in the world for casual visitors, but they would be horrified if a vine-grower turned up at their office or factory expecting to be shown around and to chat.

Felstar, FELSTED, ESSEX

GRAHAM AND IRENE BARRETT

Mr and Mrs Barrett were keen amateur winemakers and vine-growers; they had a few vines in their Essex garden. At this time, Mr Barrett worked in a printing business, commuting to London every day. In 1965 the Barretts bought 10.5 acres of land at Cricks Green, near Felsted in Essex. Graham Barrett continued his work in London while the vineyard was created between 1967 and 1974. When he left his job to concentrate on the vineyard, Irene Barrett went back to work for a while until the business was well established. They are now both fully occupied with the vineyard. Mrs Barrett has been the secretary of the English Vineyards Association since it was founded in 1967.

The vines are planted on clay and loam, 67 m (220 feet) above sea level. The Barretts' one regret is that they did not find a lower site with a lighter soil.

There was no house on the site and at first the Barretts could only visit their vineyard at weekends. 'The weeds were four feet high.' The first planting was on a third of an acre. The ground was cleared by contract. Mr Barrett dug the holes and planted the vines. The remaining 10 acres were cropped, by contract with a neighbouring farmer, with beans and mustard to clean and improve the soil. Mole drainage was carried out. Later, cereal crops were grown to keep the land in good condition until vines were planted.

Meanwhile it was becoming a necessity for the Barretts to live on the vineyard. Hares, particularly, became very bold as they went to work undisturbed to nibble the vines and destroy the grafts. It took two years to get planning permission for the house because the area under the vines was less than the 4 acres, which is the minimum if a horticultural business is to be considered commercial. However, with the Ministry of Agriculture behind them, they finally received permission.

The vineyard is kept completely weed-free by herbicides. Farmyard manure was once used, but the Barretts found it hard work without a muck spreader. Now only artificial fertilizers are used and this policy, combined with herbicides, saves them two full days each fortnight.

Twelve different varieties of vines are being grown at Felsted, all with different ripening dates, so many different wines are made in batches. The Barretts are obviously deeply interested in winemaking and are constantly experimenting. They have made sparkling wine and red wine. In 1973, they picked frozen grapes in the middle of the night of 30 November and pressed them immediately to make 32 litres (7 gallons) of the very rare and sought-after Eiswein which has been produced only very occasionally in Germany, where it sells for staggering prices.

The Barretts make wine only from their own grapes, having no spare capacity or time to make wine for other growers. They have used wooden casks for a reasonable portion of their vintage. Mr Barrett is evidently a good handyman, for the second-hand casks are beautifully restored. The bulk of the crop is now fermented in fibreglass tanks.

The Barretts have an off-licence shop at the vineyard, which is open every day except Sunday. Their wines are sold here and at various other outlets, including Harrods. They have an interest in an agency for winemaking equipment imported from Italy, including round wooden basket presses of the type they themselves use. They sell vines at the vineyard and by mail order. Unlike some vineyards, Felsted is not very suitable for large numbers of tourists. Mr and Mrs Barrett take round groups of visitors at weekends, by prior arrangement only, and are happy for any visitors to the shop, during weekdays, to take a look at the vines on their own, as long as work can continue without being interrupted by conversation.

It has taken ten years to establish the vineyard. The first small commercial crop was harvested in 1969 and was all sold to a local wine merchant. Since then the vineyard has gone from strength to strength and in the bad year of 1972, when many vineyards produced either no grapes at all or a crop of such poor quality that the wine was far from satisfactory, Felsted was able to produce a third of what should have been the normal crop. In 1978, another very difficult year, they have again achieved one-third of the normal crop and the quality of the vintage promises to be the best ever produced at the vineyard. The Barretts expect a bad year every five years and are justifiably pleased with Felsted's performance in 1972 and 1978. The vineyard is one of the most successful in the British Isles. This is an astonishing achievement on a site which is less than ideal.

Flexerne Vineyard, NEWICK, LEWES, EAST SUSSEX

MRS PAMELA SMITH

Pamela Smith grew soft fruit in her smallholding near Newick in East Sussex. She specialized in very high quality fruit which, carefully packaged, was consigned to Covent Garden, from where it went to luxury shops in London. Strawberries were her principal crop. Two things began to disrupt her business; one was transport, the other the difficulty of finding reliable pickers. In 1964, Mrs Smith bought a bundle of Müller-Thurgau cuttings and planted them out in prepared trial beds. Subsidizing her investment from sales of soft fruit and home-reared vine cuttings, she now has $2\frac{1}{2}$ acres planted with 6715 Müller-Thurgau vines, all propagated from that original bundle of sixty-eight cuttings.

The vineyard is on Tunbridge Wells sand, south facing and well sheltered; it is 46 m (150 feet) above sea level and is in a traditional fruit-growing area. This may partly account for Flexerne's consistently high yields, but Pam Smith's horticultural experience must help too. The vines are planted rather intensively, 1.2 m (4 feet) apart with only 1.2 m (4 feet) between the rows. No tractor is used, and 1.2 m (4 feet) gives ample room for the Smiths' rotavator and cultivator. Weeds are kept down by cultivating and hoeing with paraquat used in winter only. Farmyard manure, supplied by a local farmer, is wheelbarrowed about the vineyard. No artificial fertilizers are used. Pam Smith resisted spraying for years, but now she sprays Rovral from a knapsack sprayer; she has always dusted the vines with sulphur dust and Bordeaux powder, using a hand operated dusting machine.

The vine cuttings are planted 225 mm (9 inches) apart in a nursery bed. The success rate is between 85 and 90 per cent. The cuttings stay in the bed for two years, which Mrs Smith finds saves her the labour of keeping a much larger area under cultivation.

Wine is made by the Merrydown Wine Company in return for one-third of the crop. The grapes are harvested and dispatched to the winery in 14 kg (30 lb) wooden crates. In 1975, Flexerne was awarded third place in the Gore Brown Trophy competition.

Pam Smith runs the vineyard almost entirely single-handed. Her fifteen-year-old son Peter, who is at school nearby, and her husband Roy, who works full time as an accountant, give what help they can in their spare time. Pickers are enrolled for harvest, and ploughing is done by contract before new areas are planted. Roy Smith is good with machinery and maintains the rotavator and cultivator. Naturally, he also does the accounts, but Pam Smith deals with the Customs and Excise, does most of the vineyard work and deals with the marketing and delivery of the wine.

She does not gloss over the hard work involved in loading and transporting the grapes to the winery; unloading, stacking and storing the wine on its return and then delivering the wine to the various outlets.

The sheer bulk of the crops and weight involved is not to be overlooked. Harvest time is exciting but hard work with much lifting of heavy boxes: fruit has to be carried down the rows, trailers have to be loaded, and lorries loaded to transport the grapes to the winery. Empty boxes come back from the winery and need stacking, cleaning and sometimes mending. When the wine has been made, it is delivered back from the winery and needs stacking in the cellar. The actual lifting of some 400 cases that weigh approximately 33 lb each is a hard day's work.

The Smiths do not include the value of the land or their own labour in their estimate of the cost of setting up their vineyard, feeling that the land continues to appreciate in value and that their own work is a part-time labour of love.

We have been able, without sacrificing more than something like 50 per cent of what most people would term their leisure time, to plant and bring to maturity $2\frac{1}{2}$ acres of vines over some five years, paid for in the main out of the sale of soft fruits planted earlier and sales of vinestocks grown. This has been achieved without our family sacrificing its main source of income. We therefore suggest that others may find it possible.

An Foras Talúntais (The Irish Agricultural Institute), BALLYGAGIN, CO. WATERFORD

MR EAMON KELLY

Some research into vines has been done by the Institute at one of its centres in the south of the country, at Ballygagin in Co. Waterford. Ballygagin is the main centre in Ireland for pomology, with about 35 acres of apple trees. However, they also have about $\frac{3}{4}$ to 1 acre of vines. Mr Eamon Kelly has been experimenting to find a vine suitable for Irish conditions. He is passionate about vines; one suspects that the Institute is tolerant and somewhat bemused at vineyards amongst its apple trees. Mr Kelly became interested because he had grown vines in his own garden; when the subject became popular in Britain in the early seventies, the Agricultural Institute decided to anticipate future enquiries by initiating some research into vine-growing potential in Ireland.

The official view of the Institute is that it has not come up with a commercially viable vine as yet. Mr Kelly himself is hopeful that it will. At the moment he accepts that although vine growing is practical as a hobby, it is not yet a commercial proposition.

The grapes grown at Ballygagin are taken to the Agricultural Institute's centre at Kinsealy, Malahide Road, Dublin 5, where they are made into wine by Dr Michael Jelly.

Seven varieties of vine were planted at Ballygagin in 1972:

Siegerrebe. Not a high cropper, but it can be eaten for dessert. Tends to ripen too early. The experiment with Siegerrebe is not successful – the crop is too small and the wine is not of good character, a 'Muscadet' flavour should come through, but doesn't. It may have some future as a dessert grape. Mr Kelly describes the flavour as 'delightful'.

Seyve-Villard 5/276. Produced very big crops, but the quality of the wine is not good. The wine could be used as a base for blending. It crops up to 3.2 kilos (7 lb) per vine.

Madeleine Angevine. This has produced a very acceptable wine. It is a good cropper, producing 2.4 kg (5 lb) per plant. It is very susceptible to grey mould.

Madeleine Sylvaner. A poor cropper giving indifferent wine.

Müller-Thurgau. Grows vigorously in Ballygagin, but crops badly, which is a great pity as the wine quality is excellent.

Seibel 13053. A very good cropper, but produces an unacceptable wine which is too thin and has too high an acid level.

Brant. Produces high sugar levels, but it is not a good cropper. Yet it has excellent resistance to disease. Fruit good to eat when ripe.

All the above seven varieties are partial or total 'failures'. Mr Kelly considers the Madeleine Angevine the best so far, but he believes other German varieties may be more suitable to Irish conditions. He would recommend Irish growers to try Madeleine Angevine, with the proviso that other varieties may prove to be better. In February 1977, Mr Kelly planted eight new German varieties: Huxelrebe, Faber, Ortega, Scheurebe 88, Gutenborner, Reichensteiner, Rabaner, Schönburger. In Germany, where rainfall is lower than in Ireland, all these varieties have produced high sugar and low acid (the acid content will be higher in Ireland). It will be three years before results are available from Ballygagin.

Rabbits are a major problem. Also, Ballygagin is too close to the sea. On occasion, salt spray is blown the 2½ miles inland and damages the crop. Ballygagin is about 24–27 m (80–90 feet) above sea level and the average rainfall is about 1016 mm (40 inches). Frosts have not been a problem since the vines have grown up above ground level. Herbicides are used around the vines to kill off all vegetation. Mr Kelly feels this is proving successful. The herbicide eliminates competition for the vines and gives a warmer temperature; it also makes the soil more acid. He applies lime to counteract any potential magnesium deficiency. There is a widespread boron deficiency at Ballygagin, which may account for the low yields or be a contributory cause. This is under investigation.

Mr Kelly considers his six years' research as insufficient, even though he has been cropping fully since the fourth year. He says he needs ten years for a proper assessment.

Hambledon Vineyard, PORTSMOUTH, HANTS

SIR GUY SALISBURY-JONES

MANAGER: MR BILL CARCARY

Sir Guy was always a lover of France and French wine. His stepson suggested that he might plant vines in a paddock where once his daughter had kept her ponies. After reading the work of Edward Hyams and Barrington Brock, he set out with Mr Blackman, his gardener, to have a look at the vineyards of Burgundy and to consider the possibility of planting a vineyard on the south-easterly slope below his house in Hampshire. While in France he ordered 4500 vines with which to plant his 1½ acres.

The vines were planted in 1951. The first wine went on sale in 1955. Further plantings were made in 1958, 1967 and 1973; there are now over 5 acres and about 15,000 vines – Chardonnay, Pinot Noir, Pinot Meunier and Seyval Blanc.

The vineyard is on a chalky, exposed slope not far from Broad-halfpenny Down, where the first game of cricket was played. Because of the winds which sweep the site the vines are kept low; growth is not allowed above 1.2 m (4 feet), which is lower than the former practice at Hambledon. Since the vines were lowered, the sugar content of the grapes has been higher.

Various pruning methods are used, Single and Double Guyot, Chablis and Vallée de la Marne. Mr Carcary says that he has to treat each vine as an individual. Windbreaks have been erected along the western boundary to protect the vines. The original vines were planted 0.9 m (3 feet) apart with 1.2 m (4 feet) between the rows; more recently the spacing has been wider and the younger vines are 1.2 m (4 feet) apart, still with 1.2 m (4 feet) between the rows.

Mr Carcary started work at the vineyard in 1966, having been a qualified radio instructor in the Army. He says that as he had no qualifications for the job, he feels that he owes it to the postscript to his letter of application; 'PS. I am not afraid of hard work.' He learned about vineyards from Sir Guy and his gardener and has spared no pains since to increase his knowledge; he says that the effort to keep up with developments in viticulture and winemaking have improved his French beyond recognition. (Hambledon has always kept up its French connections and the vineyard is run on French lines.)

With the aid of the only French vineyard tractor in Britain, the tracteur-enjambeur, Jacquet, with its 475 cc (2 CV Citroën) engine,

Mr Carcary looks after the vineyard with the help of a girl who comes in three days a week. The high tractor straddles the rows of vines, can pull a load of 2 tons uphill and with its help Mr Carcary can spray the entire vineyard in $2\frac{1}{2}$ hours. Sixteen pickers handle the harvesting and two women help Mr Carcary with the bottling.

The *cave*-like winery is just beside the house. Here Mr Carcary showed us the electric wine press, which takes one hour to press the grapes; the gentle pressing is repeated eleven times in the hour.

The average yield is 3000 bottles to the acre. Hambledon has open days in the summer, when visitors are welcomed to the vineyard and the garden, and refreshments are provided. Much wine is sold direct to visitors. An astonishing 20 per cent of Hambledon's wine is exported; the wines have gone to France, Belgium, Germany, South America, the United States, Canada, Australia, even to Japan. The wines are also on sale locally and in many restaurants and hotels.

Harefield, HAWKHURST, KENT

DR WILLIAMS

Dr Williams can only spare a little time from his practice. When he moved to his house near Hawkhurst in Kent, he was somewhat at a loss as to what to do with his land; having laid out the garden, he still had about $1\frac{1}{2}$ acres of ground. He planted the vines in 1975 on $\frac{2}{3}$ of an acre. 'I'm hoping it will get my daughter through university.' He read books on vine-growing but found them unsatisfactory; 'Only experience can tell you the snags.'

The vineyard is on very good, deep sandy soil and slightly sloping. Most of the vines are Müller-Thurgau. The original 600 vines were bought from the Merrydown Wine Company; 150 of them failed to grow and Merrydown generously replaced them. Dr Williams omitted to note which were the dead vines; once all the vines were dormant, it was difficult to distinguish between the quick and the dead, which made replacement something of a puzzle. Growth has been rather poor because of two drought years (1975 and 1976) but the roots have been examined and are entirely satisfactory and vigorous.

Dr Williams did all the work himself at weekends. He prepared the ground for planting with a rotary cultivator and showed me how wavy the rows were, because of the difficulty of controlling the heavy machine. The posts were put in with the help of a hired post-hole borer, but he wishes he had thought of tackling this job in winter, when the ground was damp and soft. In spite of good natural drainage the vineyard suffered from some waterlogging and Dr Williams was faced with a difficult and disagreeable job – digging land drains by hand across the rows of vines (which are planted across the natural slope).

Spraying is carried out with scrupulous care and disease has not been a problem. Damage has chiefly been from pigeons. Red spider appeared and were controlled by derris dust.

The most time-consuming task is mowing the grass lanes between the rows. Dr Williams has now bought a large second-hand mower, once used by a local authority, which completes the job more quickly than his original mower.

The total cost of the vineyard has been £750; this covers:

> 700 vines at 40p and 50p
> Knapsack sprayer
> Another small sprayer
> The large second-hand mower
> Hop poles, bought from a local farmer
> Second-hand hop wire, bought from a farmer
> Plastic ties, bamboos, etc.

Dr Williams is planning to extend the vineyard to cover the remaining ground; it will then be a full acre and a half.

Longueville House, CO. CORK

MR MICHAEL O'CALLAGHAN

Mr O'Callaghan runs a country-house hotel in Co. Cork which has an excellent reputation both for food and wine. The oaks by the house were planted in imitation of the battle lines at Waterloo and the O'Callaghans have kept up the French connection by having Château Pichon-Longueville from 1961 onwards on their wine list. They also acquired the whole production of the lesser Château de Longueville 1972, in the wood, and it is now one of their draught wines. It seemed logical to attempt to produce an Irish Longueville, so an acre of Müller-Thurgau vines were planted in 1972.

The first wine was made in 1977, the grapes being harvested at the beginning of November. The wine labels have been printed and Mr O'Callaghan hopes to be able to produce enough to enable him to provide his own house wine for the hotel.

Recently he went to Germany to visit the German vineyards and research stations. Professor Dr Helmut Becker advised him to plant Reichensteiner, which should give heavier yields and ripen earlier than the Müller-Thurgau, if the German experience is applicable to Ireland. Mr O'Callaghan therefore planted $2\frac{1}{2}$ acres of Reichensteiner in March 1978.

Longueville's main problem has been botrytis, which is encouraged by the soft, moist Irish climate. Mr O'Callaghan controls botrytis by regular spraying with Ronilan, which he has found very effective even in wet seasons, such as the summer of 1977.

In common with other Irish vine-growers, Mr O'Callaghan has found that the mild Irish winter and the early spring give Irish vines a head start over the English, but the English vines ripen earlier than the Irish, because of the hotter English summer. However, Ireland has the advantage of later, mild autumns, so that harvesting can often be done later in Ireland than in England.

Marriage Hill, WYE, ASHFORD, KENT

MR MICHAEL WATERFIELD

Michael Waterfield and his wife started the Wife of Bath restaurant in Wye in 1964, and in 1972 formed a partnership at the restaurant, whereupon he and his family moved to Marriage Farm on the North Downs. Having more free time, he planted a vineyard to supply the restaurant with its own wine.

Marriage Hill is 107 m (350 feet) above sea level and the vineyard is very exposed. Its $1\frac{1}{2}$ acres slope south-east and it is swept by north-easterly winds, in spite of the black-slatted plastic windbreak which Mr Waterfield has placed 9 m (30 feet) from the vines. This gives some protection while trees, recently planted, grow up to give more effective shelter. The vines are trained low because of the high winds; the bottom wire is only 300–450 mm (12–18 inches) above the ground. The soil is chalky.

The field originally grew corn; it was ploughed and prepared for the vineyard in 1972. A potato plough was borrowed to dig trenches for the rows of vines. Rabbits were troublesome in the early stages. Mr Waterfield did not put up a rabbit-proof fence but relied on Stockholm tar, which he painted on the vines; this was ineffective and many vines were lost. It was difficult to replace the lost vines as herbicides were being used to control weeds among the established vines. Mr Waterfield was advised that the grass lanes, which he had originally, could be responsible for a potash deficiency which was affecting the vines. Weeds and grasses are now controlled by Gramoxone and simazine and the use of a rotavator.

Mr Waterfield is the only grower I have met who likes to use plastic wire (Thor Monofil) for his vines. The bottom wire is steel, but he finds that for the wires above, used for tucking in the growing shoots, plastic is softer, warmer and kinder to the vines. Steel wire, he says, tends to scar the vines, which are then more vulnerable to botrytis.

The vines are Müller-Thurgau with some Reichensteiner for sugar and Scheurebe for quality and spice.

Mr Waterfield looks after the vineyard entirely on his own, with the help of a mini-tractor (Landlord Simplicity) with hydraulic sprayer (Cooper Pegler), and assistance with bottling and pruning from two horticulturally trained friends.

Yields at Marriage Hill have not been heavy so far but the quality of the wine made from the grapes on this high exposed hillside is excellent. The varieties are blended to produce only one wine. The winery is in a converted farm building, brick with a brick floor. This is rather hard to clean, so Mr Waterfield washes it down with Milton solution. A traditional wine press from Burgundy is used; the wine is made in four vats, two holding 1000 litres (220 gallons) and two holding 400 litres (88 gallons). A carbon dioxide cylinder is used to prevent oxygen spoiling the wine when there is an air-space in a vat. The gas is transferred as needed through a length of tubing. Much of the wine is put into half-bottles. Mr Waterfield finds that many people in his restaurant like to have half a bottle of white wine with the first course and then go on to a red wine, so half-bottles sell well.

Mr Waterfield does not only make wine. He is making vermouth from a Tuscan recipe given him by his grandmother, who lived near Florence.

There was no wine cellar at Marriage Hill. An underground rain-catchment vault has been emptied and converted into an excellent cellar. Many houses have these underground brick-lined chambers, which were necessary water stores in the days before mains water was available, so other growers might find they have a ready-made cellar awaiting conversion.

Marriage Hill is a small, part-time vineyard. Without the restaurant it is doubtful whether it could be profitable; with the restaurant it seems to be viable and it certainly produces good wine.

Maryville House, KILWORTH, CO. CORK

MR NEVILLE WEALE

Mr Weale returned to Britain from Rhodesia eighteen years ago; in 1972 he planted a vineyard at his home in Ireland. Of the initial five hundred vines only eleven survived, for the vines, which were imported from England, were poor specimens and the weather was exceptionally hard. Mr Weale feels that the plants were not helped by being sprayed by the port authorities, on their arrival in Ireland, with an anti foot-and-mouth disease preparation. He has since raised his own plants and now has 550 Müller-Thurgau and 300 Seyval Blanc vines. The Müller-Thurgau tend to make too much vegetative growth at Maryville, and they bear too little fruit; they have also suffered from botrytis and a bad attack of powdery mildew. Mr Weale has also planted 850 Madeleine Sylvaner vines, hoping that these will improve the ripeness of his crop and spread the risk of damage due to bad weather. The older vines, Müller-Thurgau and Seyval Blanc, are planted in rows between ancient apple trees in the walled garden behind the house. There the soil has been well manured for the last two hundred years. The Madeleine Sylvaner are planted in a more open site in front of the house, which offers better ventilation than the walled garden. The Madeleine Sylvaner have cropped in 1978 for the first time; the grapes had to be picked somewhat prematurely due to the unwelcome appearance of numbers of wasps.

All the older vines have been recently converted from the Double Guyot system to the Inverted Cordon (a high-culture system, similar to the Geneva Double Curtain in some respects, with the main training wire at $5\frac{1}{2}$ feet above the ground). The Inverted Cordon is much used in New Zealand; it allows better ventilation than Guyot and more exposure to direct sunlight; being so high, it also minimizes the danger of frost damage – late spring frosts have been a problem at Maryville in previous years.

The rows of vines are 2.7 m (9 feet) apart, with grass lanes between; these are wide enough to allow Mr Weale to spray the vines and harvest the grapes from his Land Rover. Weeds are kept down by black polythene sheeting while the vines are growing up to the training wires. Once they are established it is intended to graze sheep in the vineyard, so long as they do not bark the vines. (I feel that Mr Weale may be a little optimistic on this point.)

The annual rainfall, while comparable to that in Britain, falls more frequently. The consequent humidity has encouraged fungal diseases and Mr Weale is the first to say that he has not yet succeeded in controlling mildews and botrytis. As far as the quality of the wine is concerned, he feels that his wine compares very favourably with wines from Britain. 'For those who enjoy wine, it is a challenge to try one's hand at it,' he says, 'But what is interesting to me is that wine produced here is unique in flavour and quite different from a wine produced from the same vine varieties in Britain or the Continent.'

Penshurst Vineyard, PENSHURST, KENT

MR BOB WESTPHAL

Bob Westphal is Australian; he met and married his English wife during the Second World War. Now the Westphals spend eight months of the year in England and our four winter months in the Australian summer. I asked Mr Westphal why he had not considered vine-growing in Australia rather than Kent. His answer: 'That would have been too easy.' He has two vineyards, one in his kitchen garden, the other is a 3-acre commercial vineyard.

The site is on a gentle slope to the south, in the low hills which surround the village of Penshurst, Kent. Originally it was scrub woodland; the trees have been cleared but the bluebells still flower defiantly along the rows of vines. In bluebell time this must surely be one of the prettiest of English vineyards. The bluebells seem impervious to sprays; Mr Westphal says that they do no harm and he enjoys having them. There are grass lanes between the rows of vines. This grass, and a layer of rubble at the gateway, keeps mud to a minimum in bad weather. The vineyard is planted almost to the bottom of the slope; to avoid the risk of a frost pocket, bracken and other growth are to be cleared from the bottom of the site to allow maximum cold air drainage.

The vines are 90 per cent Müller-Thurgau; the remainder are Reichensteiner with a few Perle. Bob Westphal uses home-grown bamboo canes from his garden and has cut and used his own larch posts for fencing.

In the kitchen garden, fifty Müller-Thurgau vines have been planted close together in three rows. The soil is good, being part of the garden. The vines were mulched with farmyard manure when they were planted and black polythene was laid down to suppress weeds completely. These vines were not watered or weeded for three years. In 1976, their first cropping year, they produced a staggering 300 bottles of wine. However, problems have since arisen, due perhaps to the choice of Müller-Thurgau (which is very botrytis-prone), the very close planting and the vigorous growth encouraged by a rich soil. Fungal diseases have been a difficulty in the kitchen garden and two cool, rather damp summers have not helped. No such problems have been encountered in the main vineyard, where the vines are planted 1.3 m (4 feet 3 inches) apart with 2.7 m (9 feet) between the rows to allow plenty of room for the tractor. The height of the bottom wire is 760 mm (2 feet 6 inches), which is fairly high. Mr Westphal finds that a rather high trellis means that the grapes are easier to pick, less liable to be splashed with mud and less liable to infection.

Birds are a menace in the wooded countryside around Penshurst. The entire vineyard is netted with a single net before the grapes ripen. The tractor brings the huge net down to the vineyard where it is laid out in a sausage-shaped roll. A team of volunteers – family and friends – roll it over the rows and a cheerful lunch party follows.

The Penshurst wine is all made at Lamberhurst Priory. The Westphals intend sooner or later to have their own winery; they have a suitable outbuilding to house it, after conversion.

The vineyard is highly mechanized – the tractors also being used in the Westphals' apple orchard. The second tractor is a recent acquisition; a bright green, articulated Ferrari, which can double around the rows of vines and swing neatly around the boles of the apple trees. The estate is run entirely by one man with part-time help from Mr Westphal. He calculates that the vineyard itself uses only a third of one man's time.

Mr Westphal says he makes a profit of 50 pence a bottle. The yields, as everywhere, vary widely. In 1976, a good year, the vineyard produced 6000 bottles per acre; its poorest yield yet has been 2000 bottles per acre.

Pilton Manor, SOMERSET

NIGEL AND ANNE GODDEN

Nigel and Anne Godden live in the manor house in the lovely village of Pilton. Below the house, which looks as though it has been there for ever, a stream rushes under the bridge; a short tree-lined drive leads to the nearby village church. A goat had just produced three kids when we visited Pilton; the Goddens drink goat's milk and sell surplus eggs from their free-range hens. They hope to produce crayfish from the stream, importing the stock from Sweden. When the Goddens bought the manor they started a poultry farm but in 1968, having discovered that they were on the site of the medieval vineyard belonging to the monks of Glastonbury Abbey, they planted a vineyard. At that time there were very few English vineyards and the Goddens had to plan without the benefit of much information. Decisions on planting distances, fertilizing, stakes and wires, the likelihood of soil erosion and the problems of marketing the wine had to be worked out from scratch with help from the small band of pioneer growers.

Mr Godden planted his vines close together, 1.2 m (4 feet) apart with 1.2 m (4 feet) between the rows. Later he allowed 1.5 m (5 feet) between rows. He believes in the intensive use of land but rising labour costs have begun to change his mind. He still does not use a tractor but now feels that mechanization is essential.

We were able to see the bottling in progress. The operation was proceeding with great efficiency and a glass of wine was always available for the thirsty. Wine is piped from the vats to the bottler by a free-standing pump and filtering machine. The bottles are filled two at a time. The corker, a local villager, operates the corking machine before putting the bottles into red plastic crates brought to him on the conveyor belt. A member of the vineyard staff had a fork lift truck to take the crates of filled bottles to a conveyor belt down to the ancient cellars, where two men labelled and stacked the bottles. This was Sunday, but work went on all day, with lunch provided for the helpers in the wine bar, a converted chicken house, now used to cater for coach parties.

Mr and Mrs Godden have a very professional marketing operation at Pilton. They make wine for other growers, sell vines to the public and to nurserymen, who sometimes market them at four times the original price. One nurseryman buys 8000 vines a year from the Goddens. They have a building given over entirely to this side of the business. The manor house is in a popular tourist area and tourists are welcome. The chicken house has been converted into a comfortable bar where visitors can sample stuffed vine leaves (prepared by a Greek chef) and local Cheddar cheese; wine is sold by the bottle and by the glass. In March 1978 200 cases of wine were exported to Italy; a considerable feat.

We did not ask the Goddens about figures. Obviously tourism is a very important part of their business and Pilton is excellently placed to take advantage of it. Access and parking facilities are good; there was an existing building suitable for conversion to provide for all the visitors' needs; finally, the house, the village and the vineyard are of great beauty.

Renishaw Hall, DERBYSHIRE

MR RERESBY SITWELL

Reresby Sitwell, elder son of Sir Sacheverell, poet and sixth baronet, and nephew of the late Dame Edith and Sir Osbert, suffered like uncle and father before him 'at one sadistic educational establishment after another': having survived the 'rigours and bullying of a private school' he was 'educated during the holidays from Eton' (during the Second World War), then served 'briefly and ingloriously' as a young officer in the Grenadiers. After an even briefer and unhappier interlude as scholar of King's College, Cambridge, Reresby pitched himself into commerce to find himself 'an insecure niche for some years in the bogus world of advertising and public relations'.

His last and much most congenial task in the Agency Game was promotion of wines, in particular French wines. In his own words, he 'ducked under the counter and up the other side' as wine merchant, naming his business "Only the Best", with the motto that ' "Only the Best" does not imply only the most expensive'. (Alas, all too often, it does!) An obvious sales line was the cheap but excellent Chianti from his uncle Osbert's small estate at Montegufoni, the enormous castle in Tuscany bought in 1909 by Sir George, father of the trio and grandfather of Reresby.

In 1965 the ailing bachelor Sir Osbert was prevailed upon to hand over to his elder nephew the vast, rambling pile of Renishaw with the bulk of the ancestral estates and attendant problems, and to retire to Montegufoni, where he died in 1969 and which, unexpectedly, he also left to Reresby. Montegufoni proved an impossible white elephant and had to be sold, and Mr Sitwell has concentrated more and more upon Renishaw, and spent less time as a wine merchant. However, he has planted the most northerly vineyard in Western Europe. When asked 'Why?' he replied 'Partly for old time's sake and partly for devilry – and after meeting Alan Rook.' Major Rook has a very successful vineyard at Stragglethorpe in Lincolnshire, only a very few miles south of Renishaw, and has been a source of the greatest help and encouragement to Reresby, who feels that 'if Lincolnshire can produce wine, Derbyshire can do likewise'.

Three trial plots were planted in 1972: in the park on a south-facing slope in front of the house and Sir George's formal Italian garden; in the walled kitchen garden; and in the 'Top Paddock', also walled and once used for exercising racehorses. The vines were Müller-Thurgau, Reichensteiner, Huxelrebe, Ortega, Forta 100 and one black variety, Pinot Noir. Ten vines of each variety were planted in each of the three plots. The most successful of these was Huxelrebe, followed by Reichensteiner and Ortega. Müller-Thurgau has not done well and Forta 100 has yet to produce a grape.

The south park plot, on thin soil over rock, exposed to the south-westerly winds and shaded for two hours a day by sycamores too handsome to be felled, has not been a success. The Top Paddock, sheltered not only by high walls but also by a belt of trees to the south, near enough to break the force of the wind but not near enough to shade the vines, has proved to be the best site. The soil is richer and deeper there, and the rabbits, which damaged the park vines, have been kept at bay by the walls.

There were further plantings in 1973. A row of Pinot Noir vines was planted along the south-facing wall of the paddock vineyard and for sentimental reasons some Tuscan vines were planted in the kitchen garden; so far these have failed to produce a Derbyshire Chianti. In 1975 the major planting was done: 500 Reichensteiner, 714 Seyval Blanc, 500 Pinot Meunier, 300 Huxelrebe and 300 Schönburger. The Pinot Meunier vines were bought in France, for Mr Sitwell found that they are traditionally grown there in the frost pockets of the Marne valley, where earlier flowering varieties would be vulnerable to frost damage. Also in 1975 came the first wine from the original plantings: nine bottles of white wine, six bottles of red.

1976 was a difficult year at Renishaw, as at many other vineyards. The fruit set well but failed to swell due to the prolonged drought. The autumn rains prevented the grapes from ripening and the soggy harvest was continually interrupted by bad weather. Nine hundred and forty bottles of wine were made, but due to errors in the wine-making, the wine, according to Mr Sitwell, is undrinkable. The cool summers of 1977 and 1978 were not helpful to Derbyshire vines. Only red wine was made, from the Pinot Noir vines planted against the paddock wall.

The vines are strong and healthy. Only eight have been lost out of the 2600 which have been planted. They are beautifully looked after by Andrew Smith, the head gardener, and, in his prolonged absence through illness, by his stalwart assistant, Raymond Marples. The training system is Double Guyot and the vines are planted 1.2 m (4 feet) apart with 1.5 m (5 feet) between the rows. Mr Sitwell now feels that he has not allowed quite enough room for vines and machines. An American mini-tractor, the Wheelhorse, is used for most vineyard work, but there is a larger Japanese Kubota tractor with power take-off for spraying.

It is sad that so far no wine has been produced at Renishaw worthy of the Rex Whistler design on the wine label and the Sitwell lion on the cork. Yet Mr Sitwell's enthusiasm is undiminished. He has proved that vines will grow and grapes will ripen in the open, 72 m (240 feet) above sea level, on latitude 53° 18' N. Whether a commercial crop can be produced remains to be seen, but Renishaw is a place where the unexpected seems natural, from the throb and clatter of the coal mines contrasting so oddly with the peace of the gardens, to the lemon-bearing trees by the row of gumboots or the eighteenth-century wooden warrior in the hall, incongruously sporting a pair of horn-rimmed spectacles. A successful Derbyshire vineyard would not seem strange in such a setting and, with the hard work and enthusiasm of Mr Sitwell and his staff, success should be perfectly possible.

'One year, sooner or later, you will enjoy an agreeable surprise to our mutual satisfaction,' he declares.

Spots Farm, TENTERDEN, KENT

STEPHEN AND LINDA SKELTON

Stephen Skelton worked for his father-in-law in building and property development until the slump in the property market. The family also had a farming business and by 1974 he and his wife, Linda, had decided to farm themselves. They now farm 35 acres. They grow apples, strawberries, sweetcorn and potatoes, sell free-range eggs and have planted almost 6 acres with vines. The vineyard is their chief interest; the fruit, vegetables and eggs are to help the cash flow while the vines come to maturity.

Mr Skelton became interested in vines in 1974. He decided that Germany was the place to learn about vines and went out to Sichel, the wine dealers of Mainz who market Blue Nun, ostensibly for a wine-tasting but in fact to ask for a job in a vineyard. Sichel have no vineyards of their own, but one of the directors of the firm, who had himself once worked on an English farm for a year, helped him to find a job. In June 1975 Mr Skelton started work at Schloss Schönborn, near Rudesheim, in the heart of the Rhine wine region, and stayed for a year as an agricultural labourer doing all kinds of work in the vineyard. He feels that the practical experience was invaluable. The vineyard that he worked in was very old, with gnarled vines set close together; all had to be hand-hoed and he could see for himself how important it was to train his own vines straight and tall, leaving access for machinery and ensuring that herbicides could be used. He attended lectures on viticulture at Geisenheim one afternoon a week and when his job came to an end he became a full-time student there for six months, learning practical grafting, viticulture, winemaking and wine-tasting.

The Skeltons came back to England and planted their vineyard in 1977 with 4000 Müller-Thurgau, 1250 Reichensteiner, 1250 Gutenborner and 2000 Seyval Blanc. Twenty-six experimental varieties were planted on $\frac{3}{4}$ of an acre. It is intended to make some red wine eventually. The rows are 2 m ($6\frac{1}{2}$ feet) apart, with vines at varying spacing from 1.40 m ($4\frac{1}{2}$ feet) to 1.10 m ($3\frac{1}{2}$ feet), according to the variety of vine. The vines are grown high on the double arch method, the bottom wire being at 810 mm (2 feet 8 inches).

Planting took six weeks of solid effort. The vineyard, originally an orchard, had for some time been put down to grass. Two hundred tons of farmyard manure plus fertilizer were applied and the site was ploughed and rotavated. Holes for the vines were dug with a spade. The soil is good and free-draining – 0.75 m ($2\frac{1}{2}$ feet) of sandy loam over sandstone – so the wet season of 1977 did the vines nothing but good. Losses were minimal. The rest of the farm had to be run meanwhile, and Linda Skelton admits that she would not like to live through those first two years again. In 1978 there were a few bunches to pick and the Skeltons made fifty bottles of wine, their first, after four years of hard work and planning.

The vines were planted in black polythene, but here the Skeltons ran into trouble. The polythene, which had been specially ordered at a cost of £600 to ensure that it was the recommended width (750 mm) and gauge (320), turned out to be low in carbon black (the substance used in black polythene for outdoor use to protect it against ultra-violet light). It therefore perished within nine months, becoming brittle and useless.

Xironet will be used at Spots Farm to protect the grapes from the birds. This yellow netting, Swiss made, is used only once and then

thrown away, thus saving a considerable amount of labour. It is com-
paratively cheap at £70 per acre, taking into account the time saved.
Xironet is supplied in this country by Compact Packaging Ltd of
St Albans, Herts, and is so light that it is sent through the post.

Marketing will be done through a farm shop and wine bar, for which
planning permission and a licence have been obtained. To sell wine by
the case from the gate, all that is needed is a £5 wholesaler's licence
and this is the way the wine will be marketed until the vineyard is in
full production.

The cost of the vineyard has been between £18,000 and £20,000,
excluding the value of the land and the Skeltons' own labour. The
winery is costing a further £7000 which seems to be good value for its
14,000 litre (3000 gallon) capacity. The price includes tanks, press
(second-hand, found in Germany), pump, filter, corker and filler. A
good building exists already; perhaps a further £3000 will have to be
spent in conversion and insulation with polystyrene. 'Without capital
behind us, the prospects wouldn't have seemed so good.'

The Skeltons do not wish to expand further for the time being, as
they want a vineyard that they can manage on their own. They feel
that the English wine industry must look to Germany and take advantage of German knowledge and efficiency. The Geisenheim textbooks
were on the kitchen table, well-thumbed, filled with the most detailed
information on all aspects of viticulture and winemaking. Mr Skelton
told me, 'The most useful thing I ever did towards viticulture was
learning to read German.' They recognize that not everyone has the
time or opportunity to spend a year or two in Germany and, of course,
it remains to be seen how far German experience applies to English
conditions.

Wern Dêg, LLANARTH, DYFED

DR IDRIS THOMAS

Dr Thomas lives in Bognor Regis, having now retired from his post as
head of a college music department. He now employs some part-time
labour and makes the long journey to his vineyard in Wales whenever
he can spare the time. He writes: 'Viticulture is simply my hobby and
an interest, but I can sell more than I can ever produce, mostly through
the Welsh Development Corporation, to assuage the thirst of Welshmen
in the USA.'

Dr Thomas has sent me the following report on his vineyard. One

can only admire his perseverance and enthusiasm; maybe he will prove
to be the Welsh Barrington Brock, for he has shown that grapes will
grow in Wales and perhaps one day they will be grown in commercial
quantities.

'This vineyard was first planted in 1964 after interest had been aroused
by the establishment of one at Trimsaran near Llanelli by Granville
Lloyd, sponsored by Mrs Gore-Browne (herself a noted viticulturist at
Beaulieu) who had Welsh connections and who was keen to introduce
viticulture in her native country. The two sponsored growers had
mixed fortunes – the vineyard planted in Pembrokeshire received scant
attention and was soon a graveyard of the young plants, throttled by
weeds. Mr Lloyd's venture received wide publicity in South Wales,
only, alas, to end disastrously when his splendid plants failed overnight,
probably, it is thought, because of salt carried on winds, which tortured
the vines to death.

'The Wern Dêg vineyard then began a career which can only be
described as calamity following calamity. Bad ploughing, attacks by
rabbits and birds, faulty spraying – these are some of the factors which
killed the initial thousand plants and destroyed the new plantings too.
Such misfortunes also engulfed other would-be growers and by 1970
only two vineyards of any size remained in Wales – that of Wing-
Commander Mathias at Lamphey Court, near Pembroke, and my own.
We were lucky if either realized seventy bottles of wine a year. The
Lamphey vineyard was run down by 1976, whereas the Wern Dêg
venture continued its unsteady progress while all around indulged in
head-shaking. Despite this, 2 acres were planted, and by 1977 we
produced, at last, a crop of grapes which weighed 688 kg ($13\frac{1}{2}$ cwt)
and gave about 570 bottles, which in English eyes was a deplorable
return, but seemed to us almost magical.

'Seyve-Villard and Müller-Thurgau were the two varieties which
gave best results, although Reichensteiner seems to be promising well,
too. Besides these varieties, we have planted Perle, Ortega, Chardonnay
and Madeleine Sylvaner. The grapes have so far been pressed by the
Merrydown Wine Company, but next year we hope to do our own.
The Welsh Plant Breeding Station and the Agricultural Research
Centre at Trawsgoed are very interested in us.

'The vineyard record is quite unique in its misfortune, but it has given
me considerable and abiding pleasure and we firmly believe that our
site, overlooking miles of Cardiganshire, is one of the most beautiful to

be imagined. At the moment, many people are interested in establishing vineyards and there is evidence of success in Gwent and Dyfed.'

General points on difference between Welsh and English conditions:

1   Climate is wetter than that of England and hill and sea fogs are
prevalent, encouraging mould.
2   Soil is, generally speaking, poorer; heavy clay making drainage
difficult. Soil cracks in dry weather; when it rains, the clay holds the
water in pools.
3   Labour is scarce in the country districts where there is sparse
population.
4   High winds are common, creating difficulties in tying up, netting,
etc.
5   To quote Wing-Commander Mathias, 'Grass and weeds of every
description grow to heights and abundance which would leave English
vine-growers aghast.'

Westbury Farm, PURLEY, READING, BERKS

MR BERNARD THEOBALD

Mr Theobald came to farm at Westbury on leaving the Navy after the
Second World War. He had a dairy herd and some arable land, but,
stimulated by reading the works of Edward Hyams on vines, he turned
his attention to viticulture in the sixties. His approach was original, for
he became convinced that the Geneva Double Curtain system, although
it had been developed in the USA, under very different climatic
conditions, was the best method for vines in Britain.* He received no
encouragement from any English viticulturists but, quite undeterred
by this, he planted a pilot plot of Müller-Thurgau, Seyval Blanc and
Seibel 13053 on the Geneva Double Curtain system in 1969 and 1970.
By 1973 he was sufficiently encouraged by the results to plant a further
8 acres of Geneva Double Curtain. In 1975 Westbury produced the
first red wine to be made in the United Kingdom for sale since the
Marquis of Bute's vineyard at Castell Coch ceased production in the
First World War. There were further plantings in 1975 and 1976, but
drought killed many of the young vines, and 7 acres had to be replanted
in 1977.

By 1978 the vineyard covered 15 acres, of which only 8 acres were in
production, and Mr Theobald had the pleasant experience of winning
quite a measure of acceptance for his Geneva Double Curtain. Twenty-

* The Geneva Double Curtain method is described in detail on pages 53–5.   .

eight different varieties of vine are being grown on GDC at Westbury, including Reichensteiner, Scheurebe, Madeleine Angevine, Madeleine Sylvaner, Müller-Thurgau, Wurzer, Wrotham Pinot, Seyval Blanc, Chardonnay, Pinot Noir, Traminer and Siegerrebe.

Feeling that the maritime climate of parts of France is more akin to that of Britain than is the Continental climate of Germany, Mr Theobald is also growing the vines of Bordeaux, particularly those of the great growths of the Médoc such as Merlot, Cabernet Sauvignon, Cabernet Franc and Muscadet from the Loire (the Burgundian Melon) and Malbec. No one else in Britain is growing these varieties.

The gravelly soil is well drained; the site is almost level. A windbreak of cricket-bat willows and balsam poplar has been planted to improve shelter. Mr Theobald applies fertilizers according to the results of his twice-yearly soil analysis, plus farmyard manure at 10 tons per acre when available. Gravel is a hungry soil and Mr Theobald finds the vines need more than the Ministry of Agriculture would normally recommend.

Routine spraying is done about once a week to ten days or less, depending on the weather and ceases only ten days before harvest. The most troublesome disease has been phomopsis, now controlled by spraying in winter and early spring. Birds are not too much of a problem in the open Berkshire countryside; black cotton and patrolling with a gun keep them away.

Mr Theobald manages the work with the help of three women, two of whom are only part-time in the vineyard, the third, Christine Preston, makes the wine. Winemaking is done in an ancient and beautiful barn. The red wine is made in a stainless-steel bulk milk container (a legacy from Mr Theobald's days as a dairy farmer), before going into oak barrels. There is a wooden staircase up to the storage loft which has been converted into a lecture room. Here slides can be shown and wine-tastings take place. Westbury can take parties of up to ninety people. Mr Theobald enjoys this side of the business; he takes the groups on a visit to the vineyard, the winery, the nursery, where vine cuttings are grown, and then to the lecture room for a short talk and slide show on English viticulture, finishing with a tasting of six different English wines. All this takes about two hours; the charge is reasonable, and, not surprisingly, Westbury is a popular place for a day out.

When 8 acres were planted with vines on the Geneva Double Curtain system in 1973, the cost was less than £500 per acre. By 1978 the cost

would be more like £1500 per acre, spread over three years. Mr
Theobald is confident of an average net profit of £1000 per acre which
he says compares favourably with £750 per acre for apples in a good
year, and even more favourably with soft fruits. With Geneva Double
Curtain, which is economical in labour and in vines, he feels that a net
profit of £2000 per acre is possible in a good year. The Westbury white
wines are good and fetch rather high prices compared to other English
wines. Apart from the sales of wine there is income from tourism, which
is being encouraged in winter as well as summer; from the sale of vine
cuttings; from angling and fish farming and from beef cattle. In
addition, Mr Theobald is considering providing courses on winemaking.
His intention is to expand the vineyard to 50 acres and harvest mecha-
nically, for which Geneva Double Curtain was developed originally
and for which it is ideally suited. If, and when, a mechanical harvester
is in operation, it will be another first for Westbury.

Wootton Vines, SHEPTON MALLET, SOMERSET

MAJOR COLIN AND SUSAN GILLESPIE

Major Gillespie was considering a second career after leaving the Army.
Mr Nigel Godden had recently planted a vineyard at Pilton Manor,
Somerset (see page 126) which is not far from the Gillespies' house at
North Wootton. It was Mr Godden who suggested that the Gillespies
should follow his example. With no previous experience, the Gillespies
planted their first vines in 1971.

The vineyard is on a south/south-east slope, once an orchard. The
rows of vines climb up the hill behind the stone-built farmhouse.
Varieties grown are Müller-Thurgau, Seyval Blanc, Schönburger and
Auxerrois. The soil is warm and the height only 21 m (70 feet) above
sea level; it is a good site. Yields are not heavy, at an average of 2500
bottles per acre, but quality is very good. Wootton Vines won first
prize at Trier with their Schönburger 1976 against all non-German
white wines, with opposition from Alsace, Austria and Hungary among
others. The same wine also won acclaim at the Dijon Wine Festival.
Schönburger vines need a good year to do well, but they have brought
much prestige to Wootton Vines.

Major Gillespie does not blend the wines from the different varieties
of vine, preferring to make three distinctive wines. This leads to higher
sales as visitors like to sample all the wines.

The winery is in the old farm outbuildings. The floor is concrete;

Major Gillespie would prefer ceramic tiles, as concrete is difficult to clean and is eroded by dripping wine. The building is virtually impossible to heat, but there is a Calor Gas blower which can be used to raise the temperature.

Wine is made in the normal fermentation vats; there is a modern press and crusher. For small quantities, however, Major Gillespie uses a home-made wooden press, with a car jack providing the pressure, and glass carboys. He will make wine for other growers who can produce a minimum of half a tonne of grapes.

Artificial fertilizers are used occasionally; Maxicrop foliar feed is regularly applied. Spraying is done every ten days by tractor; weed control is by herbicides (Ronstar, Round-up and Gramoxone). Tile drains have been laid every 10 m ($\frac{1}{2}$ chain).

The vineyard is looked after entirely by the Gillespies, with help only at harvest-time. Pruning takes them from January to the end of March – one hour to prune ten vines, including the time taken removing cuttings and tying the canes.

Wine is sold from the cellar by the bottle or the case; it can also be bought from wine merchants in London and elsewhere. The vineyard also sells Poms, a substitute for Pimms made from apples; this is popular with visitors. Tourism is an important part of the business and the vineyard is open five afternoons a week. The Bath and West Show is the chief local opportunity for bringing the wines to public notice.

Major Gillespie is cautious about financial records and chary about advising people to go into vines. He feels that microclimate is all important. 'I am sure that is the secret in this country and people must look for the right site and not plant just because they have a house with land.'

CHAPTER FOURTEEN

✿ Cellar and Kitchen

English wine should be delicate and fragrant. It is thus at its best with dishes which are not too strongly flavoured: fish or egg dishes or white meats, such as turkey, veal or chicken. It is also delicious chilled, as an aperitif, with water biscuits to nibble. It is good to drink with a summer lunch of mild creamy cheese, such as Brie, with a salad and fresh fruit to follow. There are many good drinks based on white wine. One of my favourites is Kir.

Kir

2 parts white wine
1 part cassis (blackcurrant liqueur)

Chill the wine very well and add the cassis just before serving. (Ribena can be substituted for cassis, either for economy or to reduce the alcoholic intake.)

Spritzer

A refreshing drink on a hot day and a good drink for slimmers. Have a tall glass for each person, put some ice in the bottom of each glass and fill half and half with white wine and soda-water.

Cobbler

Put some crushed ice in the bottom of a glass. Add the juice of a quarter of a lemon, a good sliver of lemon peel, a sprig of fresh mint and then fill the glass with white wine.

Summer Wine Punch

(*for twelve glasses*)

175 g (6 oz) sugar	1 bottle of white wine
275 ml ($\frac{1}{2}$ pint) water	2 trays of ice cubes
3 fresh lemons	275 ml ($\frac{1}{2}$ pint) soda-water

Put the sugar and water in a saucepan and stir over a low heat until the sugar has melted. Then boil it for a minute or two. Allow it to cool, then add the juice of the lemons and the wine. Just before serving, add the ice and the soda-water.

It would be a pity not to make enough wine to be able to use it in cooking without feeling guilty. Here are just a few ideas.

Onion Soup

1 large onion	Bay leaf
40 g (1$\frac{1}{2}$ oz) of butter	Salt and pepper
15 g ($\frac{1}{2}$ oz) flour	25 g (1 oz) grated cheese
1 glass white wine	6 slices of French bread
1 litre (2 pints) of chicken stock	

Chop the onion finely and brown very slowly and thoroughly in the butter for fifteen minutes. Sprinkle in the flour, add the wine and, after the wine has reduced, add the boiling stock, the bay leaf and seasoning. Cover and simmer for half an hour. Put the bread in a wide casserole, pour over the soup and sprinkle the cheese over the top. Put into a hot oven until the top is brown and bubbling.

Mackerel in White Wine

This dish should be prepared the day before it is to be eaten.

4 mackerel	6 black peppercorns
1 onion	1 large glass white wine

Lay the cleaned and trimmed mackerel in an oval ovenproof dish. Put heads and tails in a saucepan with a glass of water and the peppercorns. Cover, bring to the boil and simmer for ten minutes to make a little fish stock.

Finely chop the onion and scatter over the fish. Pour over the fish stock, strained, and add the wine, season, cover the dish with foil and bake in a hot oven (220 °C; 425 °F; gas mark 7) until done (fifteen to twenty minutes according to size). Don't overcook.

Put in a cold place until the following day. The juices will have set to an appetizing jelly and the dish, with a green salad and some fresh bread, makes a perfect summer meal.

Pot Roast Pork with Grapes

(serves six)

This is a very good way to roast pork, using grapes, grape juice and white wine. It comes from *Entertaining* (Sidgwick & Jackson, 1977) by kind permission of Robert Carrier.

1.8 kg (4 lb) lean loin of pork (see Step 1)
Salt and freshly ground black pepper
3 tablespoons gin
150 ml (¼ pint) unsweetened grape juice

150 ml (¼ pint) dry white wine
2 level tablespoons butter
2 level tablespoons flour

Marinade
8 juniper berries, crushed
2 cloves, crushed
1 clove garlic, crushed

3 tablespoons olive oil
6 tablespoons dry white wine

Garnish
2 level tablespoons butter

450 g (1 lb) seedless white grapes

1 Ask your butcher to skin, bone and roll a lean loin of pork. The rolled joint should weigh just under 1.4 kg (3 lb) after being prepared.

2 Combine marinade ingredients. Pour over joint in a deep dish and leave to marinate, covered, at the bottom of the refrigerator for twenty-four hours. Turn pork several times during this time to keep it thoroughly coated with marinade.

3 When ready to cook pork, preheat oven to moderate (375 °F; 190 °C; gas mark 5).

4 Drain pork, reserving marinade, and put it in a roasting tin. Sprinkle pork with salt and freshly ground black pepper. Pour about 150 ml (¼ pint) cold water around it and roast, basting occasionally with its own juices, until cooked through but still moist. It will take about one and three quarter hours, or thirty-five minutes per 450 g/lb.

5   Ten minutes before taking pork out of the oven, prepare garnish:
    melt butter in a large, deep frying-pan and sauté grapes for four
    to five minutes until golden brown. Reserve.

6   When pork is cooked, transfer to a deep, hot, flameproof serving
    dish. Pour three tablespoons gin over it, stand well back and set
    alight with a match. (Or if you find it easier, pour gin into a
    heated metal ladle, set it alight and quickly pour all over the meat.)

7   Skim fat from juices left in the roasting tin. Pour back into the tin
    any juices that have collected around the pork on the serving dish
    and return pork on its dish to the turned-off oven to keep hot
    while you finish sauce.

8   To finish sauce: add grape juice, white wine and reserved marinade
    to the roasting tin, and bring to the boil on top of the stove,
    scraping bottom and sides with a wooden spoon to dislodge any
    crusty morsels stuck there. Allow to simmer for two to three
    minutes longer.

9   Meanwhile, work butter and flour to a smooth paste in a small cup
    (to make a *beurre manié*).

10 Strain sauce into the frying-pan over sautéed grapes and, with the
    pan set on a low heat, stir in *beurre manié* in small pieces. Continue
    to stir until sauce comes to the boil and simmer for three or four
    minutes longer to cook the flour. Season to taste with salt and
    freshly ground black pepper.

11 To serve: spoon sauce and grapes over and around pork. Any
    excess sauce and grapes should be served with the meat in a heated
    sauceboat or bowl. Serve pork very hot, cut into thick slices.

Chicken Véronique

1 chicken	50 ml (2 tablespoons) double cream
275 ml ($\frac{1}{2}$ pint) made from giblets and wing tips of bird	225 g ($\frac{1}{2}$ lb) grapes, peeled, halved and pipped
Tarragon	$\frac{1}{2}$ glass white wine
Butter	Salt and pepper

Make the stock in advance.

Rub the chicken with butter, salt and pepper. Put the tarragon
inside the bird and lay it in a roasting tin. Strain half the stock into the
tin and cover the chicken breast with a piece of buttered paper.

Roast the chicken for about three-quarters of an hour in a moderately hot oven (200 °C; 400 °F; gas mark 6), basting from time to time and adding a little water to the juices in the tin after basting.

Remove the paper after half an hour to allow the breast to brown. While the chicken is cooking, prepare the grapes.

Remove the chicken; carve it; arrange it in a dish and keep it hot. Pour off the fat from the tin. Add the wine to the juices left in the pan and allow to sizzle for a minute, then add the remaining stock and scrape all the sticky bits into the gravy. Strain the gravy into a saucepan and keep hot until you are ready for the meal. Add the cream, warm it through but do not let it boil. At the very last moment, add the grapes to the sauce and pour it over the chicken.

For chicken in vine leaves, see page 146.

Grapes in the Freezer

Unfortunately, most wine grapes are all skin and pips, for most of the flavour is in or just beneath the skins, but some vines will produce grapes suitable for eating as well as for wine. In the unlikely event of a glut of dessert grapes, these can be frozen for future use; I have found the following method is the most satisfactory, but it is very time-consuming.

1 Choose grapes which are sound, firm and large.
2 Peel them. If this is difficult, pour boiling water over the grapes, leave for ten seconds and then plunge them into cold water. (If the grapes are frozen unpeeled, the skins become hard and bitter.)
3 Either pip the grapes whole using an opened-out paper clip or a hair grip, or cut them in half and scoop out the pips.
4 Make a syrup by melting 75 g of sugar in 150 ml of water ($2\frac{1}{2}$ oz in $\frac{1}{4}$ pint) on a low heat. When the sugar has melted, boil for one minute.
5 Add the grapes to the syrup and poach them very gently for one or two minutes.
6 Freeze in bags or foil containers.

Grape and Custard Tart

Rich shortcrust pastry

170 g (6 oz) plain flour	1 egg yolk
40 g ($1\frac{1}{2}$ oz) lard	15 g (1 level tablespoon) castor sugar
85 g (3 oz) margarine	25–50 ml (1–2 tablespoons) cold water

Filling

2 eggs and 1 egg yolk	85 g (3 oz) castor sugar
2.5 ml ($\frac{1}{2}$ teaspoon) vanilla essence	350 ml (12 fl oz) milk
40 g (1$\frac{1}{2}$ oz) flour	225–350 g ($\frac{1}{2}$–$\frac{3}{4}$ lb) grapes

Make the pastry by rubbing the fat into the sifted flour until it resembles fine breadcrumbs. Stir in the sugar. Mix the egg yolk with 25 ml (1 tablespoon) of water and mix it with the dry ingredients, adding more water if needed. Chill for ten to fifteen minutes.

Roll out the pastry and line a 225 mm (9 inch) flan ring, crimping the edges for decorating, and chill again before baking it blind.

FILLING

Beat the eggs and extra egg yolk. Add the sugar, vanilla essence and flour. Pour on the warmed milk, return to pan and bring to boil, stirring well. When cool, pour into flan case. Halve and pip the grapes before arranging them all over the custard.

Grape Sponge

Sponge

85 g (3 oz) plain flour	105 g (3$\frac{3}{4}$ oz) castor sugar
3 eggs	

Filling

150 ml ($\frac{1}{4}$ pint) whipped double cream	2 tablespoons chopped browned almonds

Topping

Halved grapes	1 tablespoon chopped brown almonds
Apricot glaze	

Prepare a 225 mm (9 inch) cake tin with slightly sloping sides. Put a disc of greaseproof paper at the bottom and grease again. Then flour.

Sift the flour twice with a small pinch of salt. Put the eggs and sugar in a bowl over some water that has just been boiled. Whisk until very thick and mousse-like.

Take the bowl off the heat and whisk until the mixture has cooled. Sift the flour into the mixture and fold very carefully, taking care not to overdo it. Put the mixture into a prepared tin.

Bake the sponge in a moderate oven (180 °C; 350 °F; gas mark 4) for fifteen to twenty minutes.

When the sponge has cooled, whip the cream and add a little icing sugar to sweeten. Chop and brown the almonds. Add some to the cream but keep some back for the top of the sponge.

Cut the cake carefully in half with a serrated knife. Spread the filling in the middle and put the cake together again.

Cut the grapes in half and remove the pips – they are best left unskinned. Arrange on the top of the cake and glaze with apricot jam, heated and sieved, and heated again before using.

Sprinkle the remaining nuts on top.

Stuffed Grapes

(*five or six servings*)

20 large grapes	Salt and pepper
50 g (2 oz) Stilton cheese	25 g (1 oz) almonds
75 ml (3 tablespoons)	
cream to soften Stilton	

Clean the grapes and scoop out the pips. Pound or beat the Stilton, adding enough cream to soften it. Season with pepper and salt.

With piping bag and a very fine pipe, pipe the mixture into each grape, letting some of it bulge over the top.

Chop the almonds and fry with a little salt until brown.

When cold, dip the top of each grape into the nuts.

GRAPE JUICE

When winemaking, some of the pressed grape juice can be strained, frozen and kept for cooking purposes. A liquidizer is not suitable for making grape juice. The taste of the crushed skins and pips ruins the flavour.

VERJUICE

Grapes which fail to ripen can be lightly crushed in a vegetable mill. Larger quantities can be pounded in a clean container (made of wood or plastic) with a clean, heavy, round piece of wood. The resulting juice should be strained through a scalded jelly bag or muslin and can then be frozen.

VINE LEAVES

Use vine leaves that have not been sprayed. Either take them from an unsprayed plant or use new leaves which have not been affected, and wash them well. Vine leaves are blanched for a moment in boiling, salty water before use.

It is possible to buy vine leaves out of season, either tinned, or preserved in brine, from delicatessens and shops specializing in Greek and Turkish foods. These do not need blanching; rinse before use to rid them of excess salt and be careful not to tear the leaves when folding them.

Roast Chicken in Vine Leaves

This is a way to make a dreary bought chicken taste good and make a well flavoured chicken into a feast.

1 chicken	1 dozen vine leaves
Butter	Salt and pepper

Butter the chicken. Take a sheet of foil large enough to enclose the chicken completely and rub it with a thin film of olive oil. Blanch fresh vine leaves for a moment in boiling salted water. If using preserved leaves, rinse them in cold water. Wrap the chicken entirely in vine leaves and wrap the whole thing in foil. Roast for about one hour in a moderately hot oven (200 °C; 400 °F; gas mark 6), turning down the foil and the leaves for the last ten minutes for the breast to brown. Carve the chicken and arrange in a dish with the vine leaves around it, and pour over the juices.

Game birds are good roasted in this way, so are fish which are to be grilled or baked in the oven.

Stuffed vine leaves

(*serves six*)

350 g (¾ lb) good-quality minced beef	Salt and pepper
3 heaped tablespoons long-grain rice	Vine leaves (6 to 8 per person)
Cinnamon and dried mint to taste	

If vine leaves are fresh, they must be blanched in boiling salty water. Part cook the meat, adding cinnamon and mint to taste. Cook rice for eight or nine minutes, drain. Mix mince and rice together and wrap one teaspoon of mixture in each leaf, folding leaf like an envelope. Place envelopes in a little water and olive oil. Cook for thirty minutes in a moderate oven (180 °C; 350 °F; gas mark 4).

VINE PRUNINGS

The prunings make a fragrant fire, much used in the south of France for barbecuing meat, particularly lamb. This is often done indoors on a grid over an open fire and could well be copied here, as a delicious taste is imparted to the meat.

❦ *A History of the Vine in Britain*

Three hundred and fifty years of Roman rule saw the vine well and truly established in Britain, with quite large vineyards; a site at North Thoresby in Lincolnshire, which was probably, though not certainly, a vineyard, covers 12 acres. There are terraced slopes of what was definitely a Roman vineyard at North Leigh near Witney in Oxfordshire, extending to 3 acres. Vines were mentioned by the Venerable Bede in the ninth century. As England became more settled and prosperous, many vineyards were planted by the rapidly growing number of monastic communities and also by the nobility on their estates.

This was all much stimulated by the arrival of the wine-loving Normans. The Bayeux Tapestry shows William the Conqueror's wine being loaded aboard, so he obviously was not prepared to rely on the native vintage, initially at any rate. The Domesday Book records forty-five vineyards in England. Wine was being imported in large quantities from France throughout the Middle Ages but this did not stop the English growing vines and making wine, as they had done for hundreds of years. To take the abbey of Bury St Edmunds, Suffolk, for example; in the twelfth century wine was the usual drink of the monks. Under a weak abbot it is obvious that they drank to excess, and one Abbot Samson took steps to put this right.

The abbot ordered that the houses of the sacristan in the graveyard should be utterly destroyed, as if they were unworthy to stand above the ground. And for this the cause was the frequent drinking bouts and certain things which cannot be mentioned, which he had seen when he was sub-sacristan, with sorrow and pain. So he caused all the buildings to be levelled with the ground, and within a year, where there had stood a whole building we saw beans growing and where casks of wine had lain we saw nettles in abundance. (*The Chronicle of Jocelin of Brakelond.*)

Nevertheless, this abbot, though himself an abstemious man, kept a good table with plenty of food and wine; this seems to have been typical of monasteries and large houses in the England of the Middle Ages and much of the wine would have been home produced.

The dissolution of the monasteries by Henry VIII seems to have dealt a blow to English viticulture which the enthusiasm of a few landowners and horticulturists in the seventeenth and eighteenth centuries could not cure. Grapes continued to be grown and some wine was made, but viticulture ceased to be in the mainstream of English life. Later, Victorian gardeners excelled in producing luscious glasshouse grapes for dessert, but the nineteenth century also saw an oddity; the establishment of Lord Bute's remarkable vineyard at Castell Coch, near Cardiff in South Wales, which produced wine for forty-five years and was not abandoned until the First World War.

After the First World War there was a gap of twenty-five years in which, as far as is known, no English wine was made, for the first time since the Romans brought the vine to Britain. George Ordish planted vines in his garden at Yalding, Kent, in 1939 and made wine on a small scale; he has described how this was done in his book *Wine Growing in England*, which was published by Rupert Hart-Davis in 1953. Soon after the Second World War, Edward Hyams planted a vineyard, also in Kent, at Shottenden near Canterbury. In 1949 Hyams published his book, *The Grape Vine in England*. Hyams was an eminent writer on gardening and his comprehensive and well-researched book did much to get English viticulture taken seriously. At about the same time, in 1946, a scientist, Ray Barrington Brock, planted vines at his home in Oxted, Surrey. In 1949 he published the first of the Oxted Viticultural Research Station reports. Without Hyams and Barrington Brock it is highly unlikely that the renaissance of viticulture in the British Isles could have taken place. From 1946 to 1973 Barrington Brock carried out a massive research programme at his own expense. He tested six hundred varieties of vines (of which only about fifteen proved to be successful), and experimented with various methods of culture and with the making of wine.

In 1951 Sir Guy Salisbury-Jones planted 4,500 vines at Hambledon in Hampshire and at last in 1955 the first English wine to be produced commercially since 1915 went on sale. Since then 485 acres[*] have been planted with vines for commercial production in England and Wales, an area that has multiplied nine times since 1971 when there were only 53 acres planted. This trend seems to be continuing. The English Vineyards Association started in 1967 with twenty-five members; by 1978 the membership had grown to 622.

So much for history. It is quite clear that vines have been grown in the open with success all over the warmer parts of Britain.

It is also clear that every year the processes of producing good grapes and good wine in this climate are better understood and English wine, some of which is already very good, will continue to improve. New varieties, better cultivation, more favourable sites for vines, greater interest in wine, more discriminating taste in the winemakers will all help. The trouble is that we have to acquire in a few years the knowledge of how to make wine from our own grapes, while the Germans and French have evolved their methods over a long, long time.

---

[*] This figure was recorded by the MAFF census, December 1975, since when the acreage has been increasing by about 100 acres each year; the estimated acreage in April 1979 was 800.

APPENDIX TWO

✿ *Bibliography*

BARRINGTON BROCK, R. *Viticulture Research Station Reports.* Available from Jackmans Nurseries Ltd, Woking.

BARTY-KING, HUGH. *A Tradition of English Wine.* Oxford: Oxford Illustrated Press, 1977.

BEECH, F. W. and POLLARD, A. *Wines and Juices.* London: Hutchinson, 1961.

BEECH, F. W. and POLLARD, A. *Winemaking and Brewing.* Andover: Amateur Winemaker, 1970.

BERRYSMITH, F. *Viticulture.* New Zealand: Available from the Wine Book Club.

JEFFERSON BROWN, M. *Your Vines and Wines.* Whitbourne, Worcester: Temeside Enterprises.

LENZ MOSER, DR. *High Culture System.* Published by the author, and printed by Josef Faber, 35-00 Kiems, Donau, Austria.

MASSEL, A. *Basic Oenology, Basic Viticulture* (new edition in preparation), *Applied Wine Chemistry and Technology.* Available from Wine Book Club.

ORDISH, G. *Vineyards in England and Wales.* London: Faber, 1977.

PEARKES, G. *Growing Grapes in Britain.* Andover: Amateur Winemaker, revised edition, 1978.

PEARKES, G. *Vinegrowing in the British Isles.* London: Dent, 1979.

POULTER, N. *Wines from Your Vines.* Andover, Amateur Winemaker, 1974.

RAY, C. and RAY, E. *Wine with Food.* London: Sidgwick & Jackson, 1975.

ROOK, W. A. *The Diary of an English Vineyard.* London: Wine & Spirit Publications, 1972.

SNEESBY, N. *A Vineyard in England.* London: Robert Hale, 1977.

TURNER, B. *Growing Your Own Wine.* London: Pelham, 1977.

WINKLER, A. J. and others. *General Viticulture.* Berkeley, California: University of California Press, 1975.

Other publications

Many vine suppliers provide leaflets giving information on growing vines. The Ministry of Agriculture, Fisheries and Food has several useful leaflets, including ones on drainage, outdoor grape production and liming and fertilizing recommendations.

The English Vineyards Association publishes a journal and its Newsletter is edited by Ian Paget of Chilsdown Vineyard.

The monthly magazines, *Decanter* and *Winemaker*, include articles on vine-growing in Britain, and the annual *Wine '79* includes reports on English wine.

❧ *Information, Services and Equipment*

BOOKS ON WINE AND VITICULTURE

The Landsman Bookshop, Buckershill, Bromyard, Herefordshire.
John Lyle, Bookseller, Harpford, Sidmouth, Devon.
The Wine Book Club, Woodlands, Hazel Grove, Hindhead, Surrey.
V. & E. Fleming, Stonewall Park, Chiddingstone Hoath, Edenbridge, Kent
(for antiquarian and out-of-print books).

ENGLISH VINEYARDS ASSOCIATION

Mrs Irene Barrett, Secretary, The Vineyards, Cricks Green, Felsted, Essex.

INSURANCE

R. L. Atkins & Associates Ltd, 35 Preston Park Avenue, Brighton, East Sussex.
(Mr Atkins has twenty-nine years' experience in crop insurance and is a
member of the English Vineyards Association.)

LABORATORY SERVICES

A. Massel & Co. Ltd, Weare Street, Ockley, Dorking, Surrey. Telephone
Oakwood Hill (030 679) 441/467/477.
Mark Russell, BSc, 5 Southview Road, Southwick, Brighton, East Sussex.

MINISTRY OF AGRICULTURE DIVISIONAL OFFICES

For addresses, see Appendix 9.

MUSEUMS

Harvey's Wine Museum, 12 Denmark Street, Bristol 1. Telephone Bristol
(0272) 298011.
Visitors are welcome by appointment: telephone first before visiting. The
museum has visual aids to demonstrate winemaking etc., the largest private
collection of antique winemaking equipment and tasting vessels, also
eighteenth- and nineteenth-century silver wine decanter labels. Maximum
number, fifty people.

Valley Wine Cellars, Drusilla's Corner, Alfriston, East Sussex. Telephone Alfriston (0323) 870532.
Visitors to wine cellar welcome at any time, although it is best to telephone first, to ensure someone is there. Wine cellar sells over one hundred different English wines and there is a museum including a 150-year-old press, antique corkscrews, wine bottles, etc., and vineyard paraphernalia from the past four hundred years.

RESEARCH ESTABLISHMENTS

An Foras Talúntais, Ballygagin, Co. Waterford, Republic of Ireland.
Efford Experimental Horticultural Station, Lymington, Hampshire.
Long Ashton Research Station, Weston Road, Long Ashton, Bristol BS18 9AF.
Wye College, High Street, Wye, Ashford, Kent.

VITICULTURAL STUDIES

Hascombe Vineyard, Godalming, Surrey (T. P. Baillie-Grohman).

EQUIPMENT, SPRAYS, ETC

Banbury Wire Ltd, Newington Grounds Vineyard, North Newington, Banbury, Oxfordshire. Telephone Wroxton St Mary (029 573) 210. Galvanized wire, British made, random coil lengths.
Barrett Soldani & Co. Ltd, The Vineyards, Cricks Green, Felsted, Essex. Telephone Great Leighs (024 534) 504. Telex 99452. Hand and hydraulic presses, pumps, corking machines, crusher, berry mills, etc., casks, vats, carboys. Chemical and fining agents.
Brampton Vineyard, Brampton Hall, Beccles, Suffolk. Wine tanks.
Centriplant, Gooserye House, New Road, Gomshall, Guildford, Surrey. Bottling plant and machinery, etc.
Compact Packaging Ltd, Compact House, Campfield Road, St Albans, Herts. Telephone St Albans (0727) 63453. Xironet disposable bird netting.
H. Erben Ltd, Hadleigh, Ipswich, Suffolk. Telephone Hadleigh (047 338) 3011. Vineyard machinery for the large and small vineyard.
Fyffes Monro Horticultural Sundries Ltd, Forstal Road, Aylesford, Maidstone, Kent. Paraweb windbreaks, Thor Monofil plastic wires.
A. Gallenkamp & Co. Ltd, PO Box 290, Technico House, Christopher Street, London EC2. Telephone 01-247 3211. Burettes, test papers, pipettes, titration assemblies, etc.
Heath Engineering Works (Horsmonden) Ltd, Brenchley, Tonbridge, Kent. Telephone Brenchley (089 272) 2226. Max Tapener tape guns for tying in vines, also fungicides.
B. Honess & Co., Great Cheveney, Marden, Tonbridge, Kent. Telephone Maidstone (0622) 831334. All kinds of spraying equipment.

Jackmans of Woking, Egley Road, Woking, Surrey. Fertilizers and sprays in small amounts for amateurs.

W. & R. Loftus Ltd, 1–3 Charlotte Street, London w1. Telephone 01-636 6235. Bottling equipment, presses, etc. Everything for the small grower. Staff available to give advice.

London Glass Bottling Co. Ltd, 44 Bourne Street, London SW1. Bottles and bottle recovery.

Low Brothers & Co. (Dundee) Ltd, PO Box 54, South Ward Road, Dundee. Telephone Dundee (0382) 27311. Telex 26270. Lobrene netting.

H. E. Lunken & Co. Ltd, Clarnicas, Carpenters Road, London e15. Suppliers of winery equipment.

A. Massel & Co. Ltd, Weare Street, Ockley, Surrey. Telephone Oakwood Hill (030 679) 441/467/477. Polyester-fibre storage containers; filters; pumps; filling, corking, labelling machinery, etc., presses, chemicals and finings.

T. J. C. Pearkes (Woodcrafts), Yearlstone House, Bickleigh, Tiverton, Devon. Hand wine presses, 50 litre or 2 cwt plus capacity, for grapes, cider, etc.

Rankin Brothers & Sons, 139 Bermondsey Street, London se1. Telephone 01-407 0074/4288. Stoppers and corks, capsules, etc. (Minimum order £50.)

Ross's (R.D.G.) Ltd, 23 Wardle Avenue, Tilehurst, Reading, Berks. Telephone Reading (0734) 27243. Glass containers in plastic baskets. Available by mail order.

Scott Baker Associates, PO Box 5, Hungerford, Berks. Telephone Inkpen (048 84) 342. Personal wine labels and neck labels (minimum run 200).

Sommer Allibert (UK) Ltd, Berry Hill Industrial Estate, Droitwich, Worcs. Suppliers of plastic picking baskets, boxes, etc.

🌿 *Directory of Commercial Vineyards in Great Britain and Ireland*

The sheer number of variety of vineyards making and selling wine in the United Kingdom may come as a surprise. The following information on commercial vineyards and their wines has been provided by the English Vineyards Association and by the owners of the vineyards; the list does not include vineyards which do not belong to the Association, nor does it include the dozen or so vineyards which are about to be planted or have been planted so recently that there will be a long delay before the wine becomes available.

It would have been pleasant to find a Scottish vineyard, but so far as I know only Mr John Davies of Thornhill uses some of his grapes, supplemented by imported grape juice, for the production of three to four hundred bottles a year. 'However,' he adds, 'in a few years it may be different . . .'.

NAME OF VINEYARD:
Adgestone

PROPRIETORS:
K. C. Barlow and Partners.

ADDRESS:
Adgestone Vineyard, Sandown, Isle of
Wight.

ESTABLISHED:
1968–1972.

AREA:
8·5 acres.

NUMBER OF VINES:
About 13,000.

VINE VARIETIES:
Müller-Thurgau, Seyval Blanc,
Reichensteiner.

HEIGHT ABOVE SEA LEVEL:
30 m (100 feet).

SOIL:
Calcareous drift over greensand.

THE WINE:
Made at the vineyard from a blend of
the three varieties grown. Available by
the case from wholesaler: Deinhard
and Co. Ltd, 29 Addington Street,
London SE1.

VISITING ARRANGEMENTS:
None; not open to the public.

NAME OF VINEYARD:
Aeshton Manor.

PROPRIETOR:
Chris Stuart.

ADDRESS:
Church Farm, Ashton Keynes,
Swindon, Wiltshire.

ESTABLISHED:
1972.

AREA:
7·5 acres.

NUMBER OF VINES:
7500.

VINE VARIETIES:
Müller-Thurgau, 40 per cent;
Reichensteiner, 40 per cent;
Ortega, 20 per cent; experimental:
Gutenborner, Rabaner and Kanzler.

HEIGHT ABOVE SEA LEVEL:
91 m (300 feet).

SOIL:
Loam overlying gravel.

THE WINE:
Made in Ashton Keynes, the wine is
blended and available from Oddbins in
London, Broadwell Vintners in
Gloucestershire and local restaurants.

VISITING ARRANGEMENTS:
Visits during late August and
September by written private
arrangement.

NAME OF VINEYARD:
Anglia Vineyards Ltd.

PROPRIETORS:
Mr and Mrs I. H. Berwick, Mr and
Mrs C. Knowles, Mr and Mrs R.
Knowles.

ADDRESS:
Broadwater, Framlingham,
Woodbridge, Suffolk.

ESTABLISHED:
1974, 1975 and 1976.

AREA:
14 acres.

NUMBER OF VINES:
18,000.

VINE VARIETIES:
Müller-Thurgau, 10 acres; Seyval
Blanc, 4 acres; thirteen other varieties,
experimental only.

HEIGHT ABOVE SEA LEVEL:
30 m (100 feet).

SOIL:
Sandy clay loam.

THE WINE:
Broadwater Wine is made at the
vineyard and sold through the
Victoria Wine Co. in East Anglia and
in hotels and restaurants in the Home
Counties and East Anglia.

VISITING ARRANGEMENTS:
Groups of ten to fifty-three people
from August to early October. Small
charge includes vineyard and winery
visit and wine tasting. By written
arrangement with the proprietors.

NAME OF VINEYARD:
Arundel.

PROPRIETOR:
H. B. Evans.

ADDRESS:
Arundel, West Sussex.

ESTABLISHED:
1973.

AREA:
5 acres.

NUMBER OF VINES:
12,000.

VINE VARIETIES:
Gewürztraminer, Pinot Auxerrois,
Pinot Noir, Chardonnay, Müller-
Thurgau.

HEIGHT ABOVE SEA LEVEL:
Up to 30 m (100 feet).

SOIL:
Loam over chalk.

THE WINE:
A white and a rosé wine made at the
vineyard and available from the
vineyard or Maltravers House,
Maltravers Street, Arundel, West
Sussex.

VISITING ARRANGEMENTS:
Apply for details in writing to Mr
H. B. Evans, Maltravers House,
Maltravers Street, Arundel, West
Sussex.

NAME OF VINEYARD:
Barningham Hall.

PROPRIETOR:
Michael Hope.

ADDRESS:
Barningham, Bury St Edmunds,
Suffolk.

ESTABLISHED:
1972.

AREA:
4·5 acres.

NUMBER OF VINES:
3500.

VINE VARIETIES:
Müller-Thurgau, Huxelrebe,
Chardonnay.

HEIGHT ABOVE SEA LEVEL:
40 m (130 feet).

SOIL:
Sandy loam.

THE WINE:
Riesling Sylvaner made for
Barningham Hall by the Chilford
Hundred Wine Co. Available from
Carley & Webb, Framlingham,
Woodbridge, Suffolk.

VISITING ARRANGEMENTS:
By prior appointment only during
summer weekends. Telephone Coney
Weston (035 921) 498.

NAME OF VINEYARD:
Beaulieu Abbey.

PROPRIETOR:
Montagu Ventures Ltd. (Lord
Montagu of Beaulieu).

ADDRESS:
The Vineyard, Beaulieu,
Brockenhurst, Hants.

ESTABLISHED:
1958–64.

AREA:
5 acres.

NUMBER OF VINES:
10,000.

VINE VARIETIES:
Müller-Thurgau, Seyve-Villard,
Seibel 13053.

HEIGHT ABOVE SEA LEVEL:
15 m (50 feet)

SOIL:
Medium clay.

THE WINE:
Made at the Merrydown Wine Co.,
available from the shops in the National
Motor Museum and Beaulieu village.

VISITING ARRANGEMENTS:
Organized parties can visit the vineyard
by booking in advance with The
Special Functions Organizer, John
Montagu Building, Beaulieu,
Brockenhurst, Hants.

NAME OF VINEYARD:
Biddenden Vineyards.

PROPRIETOR:
R. A. Barnes.

ADDRESS:
Little Whatmans, Biddenden, Ashford,
Kent.

ESTABLISHED:
Each year from 1970.

AREA:
16 acres.

VINE VARIETIES:
Müller-Thurgau, 70 per cent;
Ortega, 20 per cent; Reichensteiner,
Huxelrebe, Pinot Noir and Seyval
Blanc, 5 per cent each.

HEIGHT ABOVE SEA LEVEL:
61 m (200 feet).

SOIL:
Loam over clay.

THE WINE:
Made at the vineyard, the wines are
available at the vineyard shop and in
local off-licences and restaurants.

VISITING ARRANGEMENTS:
During July, August and September,
parties of between 25 and 50 by prior
arrangement; telephone, Biddenden
(0580) 291237.
The shop is open daily April–October,
10.00–18.00; and Sunday 12.00–18.00
and November–March, Monday–
Saturday, 10.00–16.00.

NAME OF VINEYARD:
Bowden.

PROPRIETORS:
Lower Bowden Estates Ltd.

ADDRESS:
Lower Bowden Farm, Pangbourne,
Reading, Berks.

ESTABLISHED:
1965/6 and 1970.

AREA:
5–6 acres.

VINE VARIETIES:
Müller-Thurgau, Reichensteiner,
Seyve-Villard, Mariensteiner, Ortega,
Gamay, Faber, Golden Chasselas.

HEIGHT ABOVE SEA LEVEL:
107 m (350 feet).

SOIL:
Reading gravel.

THE WINE:
Bowden White Table Wine is made by
Mr Bernard Theobald at Westbury
Farm and can be purchased by the
case direct from the estate.

VISITING ARRANGEMENTS:
None; not open to the public.

NAME OF VINEYARD:
Boyton Vineyards.

PROPRIETOR:
Michael W. Crisp.

ADDRESS:
Hill Farm, Boyton End, Halstead,
Essex.

ESTABLISHED:
1977.

AREA:
4·5 acres.

NUMBER OF VINES:
4500.

VINE VARIETIES:
Müller-Thurgau, Huxelrebe.

HEIGHT ABOVE SEA LEVEL:
70–75 m (225–250 feet).

SOIL:
Loam/clay.

THE WINE:
The first vintage is due 1979/80 and
the wine will be made in the estate
winery. It will be available from the
vineyard.

VISITING ARRANGEMENTS:
Not open to the public, but the
occasional private visit can probably
be arranged by writing to the
proprietor.

NAME OF VINEYARD:
Brampton.

PROPRIETOR:
C. R. J. Cadogan-Rawlinson.

ADDRESS:
Brampton Hall, Brampton, Near
Beccles, Suffolk.

ESTABLISHED:
1972.

AREA:
3 acres.

NUMBER OF VINES:
4400.

VINE VARIETIES:
Riesling Sylvaner.

HEIGHT ABOVE SEA LEVEL:
30 m (100 feet).

SOIL:
Mixed sandy clay.

THE WINE:
Made mainly at Merrydown Wine
Company. No wine has yet been
sold (1979).

VISITING ARRANGEMENTS:
Not open to the public.

Estate grown and bottled by Peter Hall
Breaky Bottom Vineyard, Rodmell, Sussex
Produce of United Kingdom 72cl
e

NAME OF VINEYARD:
Breaky Bottom.

PROPRIETOR:
Peter Hall.

ADDRESS:
Rodmell, Lewes, East Sussex.

ESTABLISHED:
1974 and 1975.

AREA:
4 acres.

NUMBER OF VINES:
4500.

VINE VARIETIES:
Müller-Thurgau, Seyval Blanc,
Reichensteiner, and others.

HEIGHT ABOVE SEA LEVEL:
45 m (150 feet).

SOIL:
Fairly deep loam over chalk.

THE WINE:
The delicately flavoured, dry white
wine is made in the estate winery and
available from the vineyard.

VISITING ARRANGEMENTS:
Not open to the public, but occasional
private visits by appointment with
Mr Hall.

NAME OF VINEYARD:
Brede.

PROPRIETOR:
R. D. Thorley.

ADDRESS:
Reyson Oasts, Broad Oak, Rye, East
Sussex.

ESTABLISHED:
1962/3.

AREA:
1·25 acres.

NUMBER OF VINES:
2500.

VINE VARIETIES:
Müller-Thurgau, Seyve-Villard.

HEIGHT ABOVE SEA LEVEL:
61 m (200 feet).

SOIL:
Heavy weathered clay.

THE WINE:
The Müller-Thurgau and Seyve-
Villard wines are made at Lamberhurst
Priory, Kent, where they can be
purchased.

VISITING ARRANGEMENTS:
By appointment; write to proprietor.

NAME OF VINEYARD:
Broadfield.

PROPRIETOR:
Keith R. H. James.

ADDRESS:
Broadfield Court Estate, Bodenham,
Hereford.

ESTABLISHED:
1972.

AREA:
6 acres.

NUMBER OF VINES:
4000.

VINE VARIETIES:
Reichensteiner, some Müller-Thurgau,
Seyve-Villard and Huxelrebe.

HEIGHT ABOVE SEA LEVEL:
107 m (350 feet).

SOIL:
Medium loam.

THE WINE:
Bodenham wine is made at Pilton
Manor in Somerset. It is available from
the vineyard, from Tanners' Wines in
Shrewsbury and from restaurants and
hotels in the area.

VISITING ARRANGEMENTS:
Not open to the public.

NAME OF VINEYARD:
Brympton d'Evercy.

PROPRIETOR:
Charles E. B. Clive-Ponsonby-Fane.

ADDRESS:
Brympton d'Evercy, Yeovil, Somerset.

ESTABLISHED:
1974.

AREA:
1 acre.

NUMBER OF VINES:
1000.

VINE VARIETIES:
Müller-Thurgau, Reichensteiner.

HEIGHT ABOVE SEA LEVEL:
91 m (300 feet).

SOIL:
pH 7 loam.

THE WINE:
Made at the vineyard, it can be
purchased by the bottle or case.

VISITING ARRANGEMENTS:
Open to public (including staterooms,
gardens, fourteenth-century church,
cider museum and Felix dress
collection) 1 May to end September,
12.00–18.00 every day except
Thursdays and Fridays.

NAME OF VINEYARD:
Bunwell.

PROPRIETOR:
Joan Goodman.

ADDRESS:
Bunwell, Norwich, Norfolk.

ESTABLISHED:
1975.

AREA:
1 ·25 acres.

NUMBER OF VINES:
2400.

VINE VARIETIES:
Müller-Thurgau.

HEIGHT ABOVE SEA LEVEL:
30 m (100 feet).

SOIL:
Silt loam.

THE WINE:
Not yet in production.

VISITING ARRANGEMENTS:
Not open to the public.

NAME OF VINEYARD:
Cambarn Vineyard.

PROPRIETORS:
Mr C. H. H. Roughton and
Mrs P. A. Roughton.

ADDRESS:
Cambarn, Dunkerton, Bath, Avon.

ESTABLISHED:
1971.

AREA:
1 ·5 acres.

NUMBER OF VINES:
760.

VINE VARIETIES:
Müller-Thurgau.

HEIGHT ABOVE SEA LEVEL:
91 m (300 feet).

SOIL:
Lime.

THE WINE:
Made at Wootton Vines
available direct from Cambarn
Vineyard.

ARRANGEMENTS FOR VISITING:
None; not open to public.

NAME OF VINEYARD:
Carr-Taylor.

PROPRIETOR:
D. Carr-Taylor.

ADDRESS:
Westfield, Hastings, East Sussex.

ESTABLISHED:
1973, 1974 and 1975.

AREA:
21 acres.

NUMBER OF VINES:
13,500. Geneva Double Curtain system.

VINE VARIETIES:
Müller-Thurgau, Gutenborner,
Reichensteiner, Madeleine Sylvaner,
Kerner, Huxelrebe and Schönburger.

HEIGHT ABOVE SEA LEVEL:
45 m (150 feet).

SOIL:
Ironstone and clay shale.

THE WINE:
The wine, made in the estate winery, is
available from the vineyard,
Merrydown Wine Shop and others.

VISITING ARRANGEMENTS:
Open to public most weekends during
summer, also by prior arrangement
with Mr Carr-Taylor.

NAME OF VINEYARD:
Castlehouse.

PROPRIETORS:
N. C. Crossland-Hinchcliffe.

ADDRESS:
Castlehouse, Plumpton Green, Lewes,
East Sussex.

ESTABLISHED:
1975.

AREA:
1·25 acres.

NUMBER OF VINES:
1000.

VINE VARIETIES:
Müller-Thurgau, Seyval Blanc,
Reichensteiner.

HEIGHT ABOVE SEA LEVEL:
52 m (170 feet).

SOIL:
Weald clay.

THE WINE:
A blended wine is made at the
vineyard and is sold by the case at the
vineyard and retail at the P.O. Store
in Wivelsfield Green, near Lewes.

VISITING ARRANGEMENTS:
None; not open to the public.

NAME OF VINEYARD:
Cavendish Manor.

PROPRIETOR:
B. T. Ambrose.

ADDRESS:
Nether Hall Manor, Cavendish,
Sudbury, Suffolk.

ESTABLISHED:
1972.

AREA:
10 acres.

NUMBER OF VINES:
8000.

VINE VARIETIES:
Müller-Thurgau.

SOIL:
Boulder clay.

THE WINE:
A dry white wine made at the Chilford
Hundred Wine Co. is available at the
vineyard's off-licence; Selfridges Ltd
and Laytons Wine Merchants Ltd,
11 Gough Square, in London, Hall &
Brambly, Fenwick Street, Liverpool
and Bentalls, Kingston-upon-Thames.

VISITING ARRANGEMENTS:
Open to public daily 11.00–16.00
(picnic site and period house). Group
tours by prior arrangement; write to
Estate Office for details.

NAME OF VINEYARD:
Chevelswarde.

PROPRIETORS:
J. H. and Mrs R. M. Daltry.

ADDRESS:
Chevel House, South Kilworth,
Lutterworth, Leicestershire.

ESTABLISHED:
1973.

AREA:
1·5 acres.

VINE VARIETIES:
Müller-Thurgau with small numbers of
other varieties.

HEIGHT ABOVE SEA LEVEL:
125 m (410 feet).

SOIL:
Sandy loam.

THE WINE:
Made on the estate, the wine is not yet
on sale.

VISITING ARRANGEMENTS:
Not open to the public.

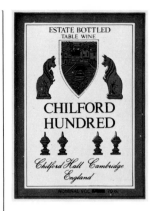

NAME OF VINEYARD:
Chickering.

PROPRIETOR:
Peter H. Day.

ADDRESS:
Chickering Hall, Hoxne, Diss, Norfolk.

ESTABLISHED:
1973.

AREA:
2·1 acres.

NUMBER OF VINES:
1100.

VINE VARIETIES:
Müller-Thurgau.

HEIGHT ABOVE SEA LEVEL:
44 m (147 feet).

SOIL:
Sandy loam and sandy clay loam.

THE WINE:
The wine is to be made at Pulham
Vineyards.

VISITING ARRANGEMENTS:
Not open to the public.

NAME OF VINEYARD:
Chilford Hundred.

PROPRIETOR:
Mr Sam Alper.

ADDRESS:
Chilford Hall, Linton, Cambridge.

ESTABLISHED:
1972–7.

AREA:
18 acres.

NUMBER OF VINES:
20,000 (on modified Lenz Moser
system).

VINE VARIETIES:
Müller-Thurgau, Huxelrebe,
Schönburger, Ortega, Siegerrebe.

HEIGHT ABOVE SEA LEVEL:
75 m (250 feet).

SOIL:
Part flinty loam, part gravel.

THE WINE:
The wine is made on the estate and is
available from Scurfields, Jesus Lane,
Cambridge; French & Foreign Wines,
10 St James's Place, London SW1;
Genevieve Wine Cellars, 167 Caledonian
Road, London N1.

VISITING ARRANGEMENTS:
Not open to the public.

NAME OF VINEYARD:
Chilsdown.

PROPRIETORS:
Ian and Andrew Paget.

ADDRESS:
The Old Station House, Singleton,
Chichester, West Sussex.

ESTABLISHED:
1972, 1973, 1975 and 1976.

AREA:
10 ·5 acres.

NUMBER OF VINES:
20,200.

VINE VARIETIES:
Müller-Thurgau, 11,200; Chardonnay,
5000 (to be replaced); Reichensteiner,
4000.

HEIGHT ABOVE SEA LEVEL:
76 m (250 feet).

SOIL:
Silt loam over chalk.

THE WINE:
Two wines (Müller-Thurgau and
Reichensteiner blend, and Chardonnay)
are made on the estate and are
available from the vineyard, local
restaurants, wine shops etc., and large
stores, including Army & Navy Stores
Ltd and Fortnum & Mason Ltd.

VISITING ARRANGEMENTS:
Open to the public each week at set
times and open days are held. Parties of
twenty or more by prior arrangement;
all details from proprietors, telephone
Singleton (024 363) 398.

NAME OF VINEYARD:
Clyston

PROPRIETORS:
A. E. Forbes, P. J. Hunt,
P. B. Miles and C. C. G. Trump.

ADDRESS:
Broadclyst, Exeter, Devon.

ESTABLISHED:
1969–72.

AREA:
3 acres.

NUMBER OF VINES:
3000.

VINE VARIETIES:
Müller-Thurgau, Seyval Blanc,
Huxelrebe, Scheurebe.

HEIGHT ABOVE SEA LEVEL:
46 m (150 feet).

SOIL:
Clay subsoil and shaly top.

THE WINE:
Made at Merrydown and Pilton
Manor, is available by case from the
vineyard and from Dartington Foods,
Totnes, and Lees Wine Store, Crediton,
Devon.

VISITING ARRANGEMENTS:
Groups of twenty to thirty by written
arrangement with the owners.

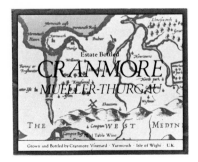

NAME OF VINEYARD:
Cranmore.

PROPRIETORS:
R. H. Gibbons and N. Poulter.

ADDRESS:
Cranmore Avenue, Yarmouth, Isle of
Wight.

ESTABLISHED:
From 1967.

AREA:
7 acres.

NUMBER OF VINES:
10,500.

VINE VARIETIES:
Müller-Thurgau, Gutenborner, Pinot
Blanc.

HEIGHT ABOVE SEA LEVEL:
30 m (100 feet).

SOIL:
Clay.

THE WINE:
A light, dry white wine made on the
estate from Müller-Thurgau only is
sold by case from the vineyard and by
House of Hallgarten, Carters Lane,
Highgate Road, London NW5.

VISITING ARRANGEMENTS:
Open to the public Wednesday evenings
in August and September. It is
necessary for groups of six or more to
book in advance. All enquiries, in
writing only, to proprietors.

NAME OF VINEYARD:
Croffta.

PROPRIETOR:
John L. M. Bevan.

ADDRESS:
Groes-Faen, Pontyclun, Mid
Glamorgan.

ESTABLISHED:
1975.

AREA:
2·5 acres.

NUMBER OF VINES:
1000.

VINE VARIETIES:
Müller-Thurgau, Seyve-Villard;
experimental: Madeleine Angevine,
Madeleine Sylvaner.

HEIGHT ABOVE SEA LEVEL:
75 m (250 feet).

SOIL:
Silt-loam.

THE WINE:
The wine is made at Pilton Manor and
is available from the vineyard.

VISITING ARRANGEMENTS:
Not open to the public but private
visits possible: for appointment write to
Mr Bevan.

NAME OF VINEYARD:
Crown Lane Vineyard.

PROPRIETORS:
C. E. and R. E. George.

ADDRESS:
Crown Lane, Ardleigh, Colchester,
Essex.

ESTABLISHED:
1974–6.

AREA:
6 acres.

VINE VARIETIES:
Müller-Thurgau.

HEIGHT ABOVE SEA LEVEL:
30 m (100 feet).

SOIL:
Light, sandy gravel.

THE WINE:
Can be purchased at the vineyard.

VISITING ARRANGEMENTS:
Not open to the public, but visits
possible by prior written arrangement
with proprietors.

NAME OF VINEYARD:
Cuckoo Hill.

PROPRIETOR:
R. O. Kinnison.

ADDRESS:
Avon Valley Nurseries, South Gorley,
Fordingbridge, Hants.

ESTABLISHED:
1972–3.

AREA:
3·5 acres.

NUMBER OF VINES:
4000.

VINE VARIETIES:
Reichensteiner, Huxelrebe, Müller-
Thurgau.

HEIGHT ABOVE SEA LEVEL:
15–30 m (50–100 feet).

SOIL:
Fine sand/clay over gravel.

THE WINE:
Four Kings Wine is made at Pilton
Manor and is available from City
Vintagers Ltd, Eurowine Distributors,
3–5 Melville Road, Bournemouth,
Dorset, and local off-licences.

VISITING ARRANGEMENTS:
Vineyard not open to public.

NAME OF VINEYARD:
Cufic Vines.

PROPRIETORS:
A. J. and Mrs E. Pinnington.

ADDRESS:
Tuttors Hill, Cheddar, Somerset.

ESTABLISHED:
1973.

AREA:
0 ·5 acre.

NUMBER OF VINES:
500.

VINE VARIETIES:
Müller-Thurgau, Gewürtztraminer,
Pinot Meunier.

HEIGHT ABOVE SEA LEVEL:
76 m (250 feet).

SOIL
Silt loam (thin), on limestone.

THE WINE:
Three different wines, from each
variety grown, made at the vineyard.
The Gewürtztraminer and Pinot
Meunier are not available, but
Müller-Thurgau can be bought from
the vineyard and from Oak House,
Axbridge.

VISITING ARRANGEMENTS:
Not open to public, but the occasional
visit possibly arranged by writing to
proprietors.

NAME OF VINEYARD:
Downers.

PROPRIETOR:
Commander E. G. Downer, RN.

ADDRESS:
Clappers Lane, Fulking, Henfield,
West Sussex.

ESTABLISHED:
1976–7.

AREA:
6 increasing to 12 acres.

NUMBER OF VINES:
5000.

VINE VARIETIES:
Müller-Thurgau.

SOIL:
Sandy loam.

THE WINE:
Will be made at Merrydown Wine
Company and be available from the
vineyard.

VISITING ARRANGEMENTS:
Not open to the public.

NAME OF VINEYARD:
Dunsley House.

PROPRIETOR:
Dr E. I. Garratt.

ADDRESS:
Kinver, Stourbridge, West Midlands.

ESTABLISHED:
1973 onwards.

AREA:
0 ·75 acre.

NUMBER OF VINES:
800.

VINE VARIETIES:
Madeleine Angevine, Bacchus,
Müller-Thurgau, Seyval,
Gewürztraminer, Siegerrebe, Optima.

HEIGHT ABOVE SEA LEVEL:
105 m (350 feet).

SOIL:
Sandy.

THE WINE:
The wine—Château Dunsley—is made
in conjunction with the local wine
society and is not commercial. It is
shared amongst the helpers, and the
vineyard is run by the proprietor as a
cooperative with the local wine society.
It is not planned to turn commercial.

VISITING ARRANGEMENTS:
Not open to the public.

NAME OF VINEYARD:
Elmham Park.

PROPRIETOR:
R. S. Don; Manager: A. G. Bell.

ADDRESS:
North Elmham, Dereham, Norfolk.

ESTABLISHED:
1970–5.

AREA:
7 ·5 acres.

NUMBER OF VINES:
8000.

VINE VARIETIES:
Müller-Thurgau, Ortega,
Reichensteiner, Huxelrebe, Kerner,
Pinot Gris, Chardonnay, Madeleine
Angevine, Scheurebe.

HEIGHT ABOVE SEA LEVEL:
43 m (140 feet).

SOIL:
Flinty loam.

THE WINE:
Dry white table wine made on the
estate available from the vineyard, and
in London at Harrods, Grants of St
James's Ltd and some branches of
the Victoria Wine Co.

VISITING ARRANGEMENTS:
Parties by prior appointment; write to
the vineyard.

NAME OF VINEYARD:
Ent House.

PROPRIETORS:
R. W. and G. L. Baker.

ADDRESS:
Ropley, Alresford, Hants.

ESTABLISHED:
Planting 1979.

AREA:
3 acres.

VINE VARIETIES:
Müller-Thurgau, Reichensteiner,
Huxelrebe.

HEIGHT ABOVE SEA LEVEL:
135 m (450 feet).

SOIL:
Clay loam over chalk.

THE WINE:
Not yet in production.

VISITING ARRANGEMENTS:
Not open to the public.

NAME OF VINEYARD:
Erdelega.

PROPRIETOR:
P. E. Brunning.

ADDRESS:
Orchard Meadow, Harts Lane,
Ardleigh, Colchester, Essex.

ESTABLISHED:
1970 to present.

AREA:
0 ·35 acre.

NUMBER OF VINES:
500.

VINE VARIETIES:
Siegerrebe, Müller-Thurgau,
Madeleine Angevine, Seyval Blanc,
Scheurebe and others.

HEIGHT ABOVE SEA LEVEL:
37 m (120 feet).

SOIL:
Glacial gravel loam.

THE WINE:
A blend of the varieties grown is made
at Horam Manor (*q.v.*), where it is on
sale. It can also be purchased at the
Corn Dolly restaurant, Great
Bardfield, Braintree, Essex.

VISITING ARRANGEMENTS:
No arrangements for visitors at present.

FELSTAR®
ENGLISH TABLE WINE
1977
Seyval Blanc
& Chardonnay
70 cl. 'e'
Produced and Estate Bottled by
J. G. & I. M. BARRETT,
The Vineyards, Crick's Green, Felsted, Essex, England.
Produce of United Kingdom.

NAME OF VINEYARD:
Felstar.

PROPRIETORS:
J. G. and I. M. Barrett.

ADDRESS:
The Vineyards, Cricks Green, Felsted,
Dunmow, Essex.

ESTABLISHED:
1967–74.

AREA:
10 ·5 acres.

NUMBER OF VINES:
14,000.

VINE VARIETIES:
Müller-Thurgau, Seyval Blanc,
Madeleine Angevine, Madeleine
Sylvaner, Pinot Noir, Chardonnay,
Wrotham Pinot, Scheurebe,
Reichensteiner, Moıio-Muskat,
Traminer and Siegerrebe.

HEIGHT ABOVE SEA LEVEL:
67 m (220 feet).

SOIL:
Heavy loam scattered with flint stones
over seam of clay and limestone.

THE WINE:
A range of wines is made on the estate
and available direct from the vineyard
and various outlets in East Anglia.
Also Harrods, London, Merrydown
Wine Company, Horam, Heathfield,
East Sussex, and Valley Wine Cellars,
Alfriston, Polegate, East Sussex.

NAME OF VINEYARD:
Fenlandia.

PROPRIETOR:
T. Lisher.

ADDRESS:
Twenty Pence Road, Cottenham,
Cambridge.

ESTABLISHED:
1977 and 1978.

AREA:
0 ·75 acre with 6 acres available.

NUMBER OF VINES:
850.

VINE VARIETIES:
Müller-Thurgau and four experimental
varieties.

HEIGHT ABOVE SEA LEVEL:
Zero.

SOIL:
Organic; clay loam.

THE WINE:
Not yet in production.

VISITING ARRANGEMENTS:
Not open to the pubic.

VISITING ARRANGEMENTS:
Groups by arrangement and conducted
visits at weekends. Prior booking
essential. Apply to Vineyard Shop,
telephone Great Leighs (024 534) 504.
Visitors to the shop can look around on
their own.

NAME OF VINEYARD:
Finn Valley Vineyard.

PROPRIETOR:
C. Clark.

ADDRESS:
Cherrybank Estates, Otley, Ipswich,
Suffolk.

ESTABLISHED:
1972, 1973 and 1976.

AREA:
10 acres.

NUMBER OF VINES:
10,000.

VINE VARIETIES:
Müller-Thurgau, 9000; Pinot Noir,
1000.

HEIGHT ABOVE SEA LEVEL:
37–52 m (120–170 feet).

SOIL:
Heavy boulder clay.

THE WINE:
A dry and a medium dry wine are
made, and both are available from the
English Wine Shop, Otley.

VISITING ARRANGEMENTS:
Parties by appointment, write to
proprietor. Open to the public one or
two weekends each year.

NAME OF VINEYARD:
Flexerne.

PROPRIETORS:
Pamela and Roy Smith.

ADDRESS:
Fletching Common, Newick, Lewes,
East Sussex.

ESTABLISHED:
From 1964.

AREA:
2·5 acres.

NUMBER OF VINES:
6715.

VINE VARIETIES:
Müller-Thurgau.

HEIGHT ABOVE SEA LEVEL:
46 m (150 feet).

SOIL:
Tunbridge Wells sand.

THE WINE:
Made by the Merrydown Wine
Company, it can be bought by the case
from the vineyard and from Army &
Navy Stores Ltd and Fortnum &
Mason Ltd in London, and from
Lewes Wine Centre, High Street,
Lewes, East Sussex.

VISITING ARRANGEMENTS:
Not generally open to the public but
visitors and groups of ten to
twenty-five may look round by
appointment only; telephone
Newick (082 572) 2548.

NAME OF VINEYARD:
Frensham Manor.

ADDRESS:
Oakleigh Farms (Surrey) Ltd,
Clements Farm, Wheatley, Bordon,
Hants.

AREA:
1 ·5 acres.

HEIGHT ABOVE SEA LEVEL:
122 m (400 feet).

THE WINE:
Made by the Merrydown Wine
Company.

VISITING ARRANGEMENTS:
Not open to the public.

NAME OF VINEYARD:
Frithsden.

PROPRIETORS:
Peter and Ann Latchford.

ADDRESS:
Frithsden, Berkhamsted, Hertfordshire.

ESTABLISHED:
1971.

AREA:
3 acres.

NUMBER OF VINES:
2700.

VINE VARIETIES:
Müller-Thurgau, Madeleine Angevine,
Madeleine Sylvaner, Pinot Noir,
Chardonnay, Reichensteiner and Faber.

HEIGHT ABOVE SEA LEVEL:
120 m (400 feet).

SOIL:
Heavy loam with flints over chalky
subsoil.

THE WINE:
The wine is made at the Gamlingay
Vineyard and is available from 38
Crouchfield, Hemel Hempstead, Herts.

VISITING ARRANGEMENTS:
Not open to the public but weekend
tours of the vineyard can be arranged
in advance by writing to the
proprietors at 38 Crouchfield, Hemel
Hempstead, Herts.

NAME OF VINEYARD:
Frogmore.

PROPRIETORS:
Mr and Mrs P. Higgs.

ADDRESS:
Bradfield, Reading, Berkshire.

ESTABLISHED:
1970.

AREA:
3 acres.

NUMBER OF VINES:
3000 plus.

VINE VARIETIES:
Seyval Blanc, Müller-Thurgau.

HEIGHT ABOVE SEA LEVEL:
61 m (200 feet).

SOIL:
Sandy loam.

THE WINE:
Frogmore table wine is produced at
Merrydown Wine Company and is
available direct from the vineyard.

VISITING ARRANGEMENTS:
The vineyard is not open to the public.

NAME OF VINEYARD:
Fyfield Hall.

PROPRIETOR:
R. J. White.

ADDRESS:
Fyfield Hall, Ongar, Essex.

ESTABLISHED:
1976 onwards.

AREA:
5 acres.

NUMBER OF VINES:
3000.

VINE VARIETIES:
Müller-Thurgau, Huxelrebe, Ortega,
Zweigeltrebe (red), Madeleine
Angevine.

HEIGHT ABOVE SEA LEVEL:
50 m (180 feet).

SOIL:
London clay and chalk.

THE WINE:
Made at Merrydown Wine Company,
available from the vineyard and
Fyfield Stores.

VISITING ARRANGEMENTS:
Not open to the public, but private
visits by arrangement only with
Mr White.

NAME OF VINEYARD:
Gamlingay.

PROPRIETORS:
G. P. and N. Reece.

ADDRESS:
Drove Road, Gamlingay, Sandy, Beds.
(Note: this is the postal address;
Gamlingay is actually in
Cambridgeshire.)

ESTABLISHED:
1970.

AREA:
10 acres.

NUMBER OF VINES:
20,000.

VINE VARIETIES:
Müller-Thurgau, Scheurebe,
Reichensteiner.

HEIGHT ABOVE SEA LEVEL:
61 m (200 feet).

SOIL:
Light and sandy.

THE WINE:
A white and a rosé wine are made on
the estate and are available from the
vineyard; the Wine Society, Stevenage;
Peter Dominic, Cambridge; and Army
& Navy Stores Ltd in London.

VISITING ARRANGEMENTS:
Groups of thirty to fifty by prior
written arrangement with proprietors.

NAME OF VINEYARD:
Genesis Green.

PROPRIETORS:
M. H. C. Fuller and Col. F. and Mrs
Y. Fuller.

ADDRESS:
Fuller Roope Partnership,
Wickhambrook, Newmarket, Suffolk.

ESTABLISHED:
1973.

AREA:
5 acres.

VINE VARIETIES:
Müller-Thurgau with trial rows of six
other varieties.

HEIGHT ABOVE SEA LEVEL:
120 m (400 feet).

SOIL:
Clay and loam.

THE WINE:
The wines may be purchased direct or
by mail order from the vineyard, and
from the English Wine Shop, Otley,
Ipswich, Suffolk; Denbar Wines, Long
Crendon, Aylesbury, Bucks; Angel
Hotel, Bury St Edmunds; and The
Refectory, Richmond, Surrey.

VISITING ARRANGEMENTS:
Not open to the public, but visits by
parties of not less than fifteen people
are possible by prior arrangement with
the proprietors.

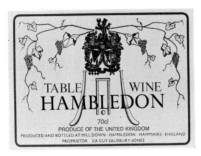

NAME OF VINEYARD:
Hambledon.

PROPRIETORS:
Major General Sir Guy and Lady
Salisbury-Jones; Manager Mr W.
Carcary.

ADDRESS:
Mill Down, Hambledon, Portsmouth,
Hants.

ESTABLISHED:
1951, 1958, 1968, 1973.

AREA:
5·2 acres.

NUMBER OF VINES:
15,000.

VINE VARIETIES:
Seyval Blanc, Pinot Noir, Pinot
Meunier, Chardonnay.

HEIGHT ABOVE SEA LEVEL:
104 m (340 feet).

SOIL:
Shallow silty loam on chalk.

THE WINE:
Two blended wines are made on the
estate and available from Peter
Dominic, London, Southampton and
Winchester; Arthur Purchase & Son,
Chichester; English Wine Shop,
Ipswich.

VISITING ARRANGEMENTS:
Open to public on certain days from
July to October; refreshments available,
free coach and car park. All details
from the vineyard, telephone
Hambledon (070 132) 475.

NAME OF VINEYARD:
Harling.

PROPRIETORS:
Mr and Mrs J. K. Miljkovic.

ADDRESS:
Eastfield House, East Harling,
Norwich, Norfolk.

ESTABLISHED:
1972.

AREA:
6 acres.

NUMBER OF VINES:
7800.

VINE VARIETIES:
Müller-Thurgau.

HEIGHT ABOVE SEA LEVEL:
122 m (400 feet).

SOIL:
Light and sandy.

THE WINE:
Harling white table wine is made at
Otley in Suffolk, and can be bought
from the vineyard.

VISITING ARRANGEMENTS:
Not open to public, but visitors welcome
by written appointment with
proprietors.

NAME OF VINEYARD:
Hascombe Vineyard.

PROPRIETOR:
Lt Cdr T. P. Baillie Grohman.

ADDRESS:
Hascombe, Godalming, Surrey.

AREA:
5–6 acres.

VINE VARIETIES:
Various.

HEIGHT ABOVE SEA LEVEL:
105 m (350 feet).

THE WINE:
Made on site. Sold in Harrods and various wine stores and at the vineyard.

VISITING ARRANGEMENTS:
Not open to the public, but Lt Cdr Baillie Grohman does run viticulture courses (see page 154).

NAME OF VINEYARD:
Hendred.

PROPRIETORS:
Malcolm and Mary Mackinnon.

ADDRESS:
Corner House, Allins Lane, East Hendred, Wantage, Oxon.

AREA:
3 acres.

NUMBER OF VINES:
3000.

VINE VARIETIES:
Reichensteiner, Zweigeltrebre.

SOIL:
Greensand.

THE WINE:
Made on the estate and at Merrydown Wine Company, and can be purchased from the vineyard.

VISITING ARRANGEMENTS:
Not open to the public.

NAME OF VINEYARD:
Henny.

PROPRIETOR:
S. R. Copley.

ADDRESS:
The Old Rectory, Little Henny,
Sudbury, Suffolk.

ESTABLISHED:
1975.

AREA:
1 acre.

NUMBER OF VINES:
1500.

VARIETY:
Müller-Thurgau.

HEIGHT ABOVE SEA LEVEL:
61 m (200 feet).

SOIL:
Loam on clay.

THE WINE:
Made at Merrydown Wine Company,
the wine is available from the vineyard,
local pubs and the Merrydown Wine
Shop.

ARRANGEMENTS FOR VISITING:
No special arrangements, but possibly
by written request to the proprietor.

NAME OF VINEYARD:
Heywood.

PROPRIETORS:
Mr and Mrs Aikman.

ADDRESS:
Holly Farm, The Heywood, Diss,
Norfolk.

ESTABLISHED:
1977.

AREA:
3 acres.

NUMBER OF VINES:
2300.

VINE VARIETIES:
Müller-Thurgau, Ruländer, Madeleine
Sylvaner.

HEIGHT ABOVE SEA LEVEL:
32 m (105 feet).

SOIL:
Fine sandy loam.

THE WINE:
Not yet in production.

VISITING ARRANGEMENTS:
Private visits at weekends from April to
October by arrangement with
proprietors, telephone Diss
(0379) 2461 or 01-340 9635.

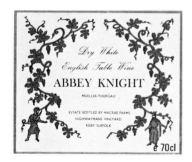

NAME OF VINEYARD:
Highwaymans Vineyard.

PROPRIETOR:
Macrae Farms Ltd.

ADDRESS:
Heath Barn Farm, Bury St Edmunds, Suffolk.

ESTABLISHED:
1974 and 1976.

AREA:
25 acres.

NUMBER OF VINES:
25,000.

VINE VARIETIES:
Müller-Thurgau, Gewürtztraminer, Perle, Pinot Noir, Huxelrebe, Optima, Bacchus, Ruländer, Madeleine Angevine.

HEIGHT ABOVE SEA LEVEL:
45 m (150 feet).

SOIL:
Sandy loam.

THE WINE:
The wine is made in the estate winery and is available direct from the vineyard, or from Rutters, 18 Angel Hill, Bury St Edmunds, Suffolk.

VISITING ARRANGEMENTS:
Not open to the public.

NAME OF VINEYARD:
Hoe Vineyard.

PROPRIETOR:
Charles Gordon.

ADDRESS:
Hoe House, Francis Field, Peaslake, Guildford, Surrey.

ESTABLISHED:
1973–4.

AREA:
0·33–0·5 acre.

NUMBER OF VINES:
450.

VINE VARIETIES:
Seyval Blanc, Müller-Thurgau, Schönburger.

HEIGHT ABOVE SEA LEVEL:
152 m (500 feet).

SOIL:
Sandy loam.

THE WINE:
The wine so far is used mainly in the production of the special English vineyard mustard produced by Mr Gordon, which is available from good grocers and some wine shops throughout the country.

ARRANGEMENTS FOR VISITING:
Not open to the public.

NAME OF VINEYARD:
Horam Manor.

PROPRIETORS:
Merrydown Wine Company Ltd.

ADDRESS:
Horam, Heathfield, East Sussex.

ESTABLISHED:
1969–76.

AREA:
0 ·7 acre.

NUMBER OF VINES:
1400.

VINE VARIETIES:
Müller-Thurgau, Huxelrebe, Kerner,
Faber, Reichensteiner, Pinot Noir,
Riesling, Ehrenfelser, Zweigeltrebe,
Madeleine Angevine.

HEIGHT ABOVE SEA LEVEL:
61 m (200 feet).

SOIL:
Sand on sandstone.

THE WINE:
Horam Manor wine is made on the
estate in the modern winery and can be
purchased at the Merrydown Wine
Shop.

VISITING ARRANGEMENTS:
Visitors are welcome to the wine shop.
There are conducted tours daily from
Monday to Friday, including, for a
small charge, a visit to the vineyard,
vinegar and cider plant, winery, etc.,
and tasting of wine, fruit wine and
cider. Telephone Horam Road
(043 53) 2401 for details.

NAME OF VINEYARD:
Ightham.

PROPRIETORS:
J. M. B. and K. R. Corfe.

ADDRESS:
Ashwell House, Ivy Hatch, Sevenoaks,
Kent.

ESTABLISHED:
1972–5.

AREA:
3 acres.

NUMBER OF VINES:
2500.

VINE VARIETIES:
Müller-Thurgau, Reichensteiner,
Huxelrebe, Schönburger.

HEIGHT ABOVE SEA LEVEL:
91 m (300 feet).

SOIL:
Sandy loam.

THE WINE:
The white table wine is made in
Lamberhurst Priory winery and is
distributed solely by Laurence Hayward
Ltd, 11 Gough Square, London EC4.

VISITING ARRANGEMENTS:
Not open to the public.

NAME OF VINEYARD:
The Isle of Ely Vineyard.

PROPRIETOR:
Norman J. Sneesby.

ADDRESS:
Wilburton, Ely, Cambridgeshire.

ESTABLISHED:
1972.

AREA:
2·5 acres.

NUMBER OF VINES:
4000.

VINE VARIETIES:
Müller-Thurgau, Madeleine Angevine, Chardonnay, Pinot Meunier and twelve others.

HEIGHT ABOVE SEA LEVEL:
15–20 m (30–70 feet).

SOIL:
Sandy clay loam.

THE WINE:
Made at Merrydown Wine Company, the St Etheldreda Wines are available from the vineyard and Merrydown Wine Shop.

VISITING ARRANGEMENTS:
Group visits by appointment during spring and summer, with a lecture tour, photographic display and wine-tastings. Good parking.

NAME OF VINEYARD:
Jesses Vineyard.

PROPRIETORS:
Major and Mrs R. Beck.

ADDRESS:
Dinton, Salisbury, Wiltshire.

ESTABLISHED:
1977 onwards.

AREA:
Up to 1 acre.

NUMBER OF VINES:
480 planted, with 600 being planted in 1979.

VINE VARIETIES:
Müller-Thurgau, Triomphe d'Alsace, Madeleine Angevine, Siegerrebe.

HEIGHT ABOVE SEA LEVEL:
90 m (300 feet).

SOIL:
Greensand.

THE WINE:
Not yet in production.

VISITING ARRANGEMENTS:
Not open to the public, but the occasional visit possible by prior arrangement with Major and Mrs Beck.

NAME OF VINEYARD:
Kelsale.

PROPRIETOR:
J. T. Edgerley.

ADDRESS:
Kelsale, Saxmundham, Suffolk.

ESTABLISHED:
1967–9.

AREA:
1 ·25–2 ·5 acres.

NUMBER OF VINES:
3900 plus.

VINE VARIETIES:
Müller-Thurgau, Seyval Blanc,
Madeleine Angevine, Bacchus and
others.

HEIGHT ABOVE SEA LEVEL:
30 m (100 feet).

SOIL:
Clay and loam.

THE WINE:
Made at Pulham Market, the wine is
distributed by Sole Bay Brewery,
Southwold, Suffolk.

VISITING ARRANGEMENTS:
Not open to the public, but private
visits by prior arrangement with
Mr Edgerley.

NAME OF VINEYARD:
Kentish Vineyards.

PROPRIETORS:
L. T. Bates and G. Watson.

ADDRESS:
Cherry Hill, Nettlestead, Maidstone,
Kent.

ESTABLISHED:
1965 and 1973.

AREA:
2 ·5 acres.

NUMBER OF VINES:
7000.

VINE VARIETIES:
90 per cent Müller-Thurgau, 10 per
cent Seibel, Seyve-Villard and
Riesling.

HEIGHT ABOVE SEA LEVEL:
45 m (150 feet).

SOIL:
Greensand over clay at 1 m (3 feet).

THE WINE:
Three white wines and a rosé are made
at Lamberhurst Priory and available
from the vineyard, local shops and
national distributors.

VISITING ARRANGEMENTS:
Parties up to fifty, strictly by
appointment and during July, August
and September.

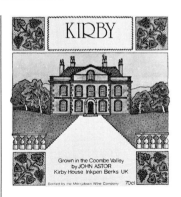

NAME OF VINEYARD:
Kingston.

PROPRIETORS:
Merrydown Wine Co. Ltd.

ADDRESS:
Chiddingly Road, Horam, Heathfield,
East Sussex.

ESTABLISHED:
1963–9.

AREA:
1 ·5 acres.

NUMBER OF VINES:
3000.

VINE VARIETIES:
Müller-Thurgau, Huxelrebe,
Mariensteiner.

HEIGHT ABOVE SEA LEVEL:
61 m (200 feet).

SOIL:
Clay.

THE WINE:
Made in the Merrydown Wine
Company's large, modern winery and
available from the Merrydown Wine
Shop.

ARRANGEMENTS FOR VISITING:
See Horam Manor.

NAME OF VINEYARD:
Kirby.

PROPRIETOR:
Hon. John Astor.

ADDRESS:
Kirby Farm Office, Inkpen,
Berkshire.

ESTABLISHED:
1971–6.

AREA:
4 acres.

NUMBER OF VINES:
Several thousand.

VINE VARIETIES:
Seibel, Müller-Thurgau,
Reichensteiner.

HEIGHT ABOVE SEA LEVEL:
197 m (650 feet).

SOIL:
Loam over chalk.

THE WINE:
Dry white and rosé wines are made at
Merrydown Wine Company; available
from estate or Spaekman, Hungerford.

VISITING ARRANGEMENTS:
Not open to public but occasionally for
private visits by appointment only.

NAME OF VINEYARD:
Knowle Hill.

PROPRIETOR:
Mr I. A. Grant.

ADDRESS:
Knowle Hill Farm, Ulcombe,
Maidstone, Kent.

ESTABLISHED:
1970 to 1979.

AREA:
3 acres.

NUMBER OF VINES:
3600.

VINE VARIETIES:
Müller-Thurgau, Pinot Noir.

SOIL:
Loam/chalk.

THE WINE:
The wine is made at Lamberhurst
Priory but is not available to the
public.

VISITING ARRANGEMENTS:
Private venture, not open to the public.

NAME OF VINEYARD:
La Mare.

PROPRIETORS:
R. H. Blayney and Mrs A. M. Blayney.

ADDRESS:
Elms Farm, St Mary, Jersey, Channel
Islands.

ESTABLISHED:
1972–9.

AREA:
6·5 acres.

NUMBER OF VINES:
8500.

VINE VARIETIES:
Müller-Thurgau, Huxelrebe,
Scheurebe, Reichensteiner, Seyval.

HEIGHT ABOVE SEA LEVEL:
91 m (300 feet).

SOIL:
Light loam over gravel.

THE WINE:
Clos de la Mare is made on the estate,
and is available from the vineyard and
by mail order.

VISITING ARRANGEMENTS:
Visitors welcome from mid-May to
the end of September, Monday to
Friday.

NAME OF VINEYARD:
Lamberhurst Vineyards.

PROPRIETOR:
K. McAlpine.

ADDRESS:
Ridge Farm, Lamberhurst, Tunbridge
Wells, Kent.

ESTABLISHED:
1972.

AREA:
25 acres.

NUMBER OF VINES:
28,000.

VINE VARIETIES:
Müller-Thurgau, Seyval Blanc,
Reichensteiner, Schönburger and
others experimentally.

HEIGHT ABOVE SEA LEVEL:
80 m (250 feet).

SOIL:
Wadhurst clay/Tunbridge Wells sand.

THE WINE:
Made in the estate winery, the four
wines are available from the vineyard
and various shops and hotels
throughout Britain.

VISITING ARRANGEMENTS:
Open to the public during summer,
details available from the vineyard
office.

NAME OF VINEYARD:
Langham.

PROPRIETORS:
Langham Fruit Farms Ltd.

ADDRESS:
Langham, Colchester, Essex.

ESTABLISHED:
1973.

AREA:
4 acres.

NUMBER OF VINES:
6000.

VINE VARIETIES:
Müller-Thurgau.

HEIGHT ABOVE SEA LEVEL:
75 m (240 feet).

SOIL:
Sandy gravel.

THE WINE:
Light white wine made in Suffolk and
Sussex is available from the
vineyard.

VISITING ARRANGEMENTS:
Not open to the public.

NAME OF VINEYARD:
Lexham Hall.

PROPRIETORS:
W. R. B. Foster and Partners.

ADDRESS:
King's Lynn, Norfolk.

ESTABLISHED:
1975 and 1978.

AREA:
8 acres.

NUMBER OF VINES:
11,000.

VINE VARIETIES:
Müller-Thurgau, Reichensteiner, Scheurebe, Madeleine Angevine.

HEIGHT ABOVE SEA LEVEL:
37 m (120 feet).

SOIL:
Sandy loam.

THE WINE:
Made in the estate winery, the wine is available from the estate office, Post Office Stores, Litcham, and Hill's Home Supplies, Blakeney.

VISITING ARRANGEMENTS:
Not open to the public, but parties by appointment.

NAME OF VINEYARD:
Lincoln City Vineyard.

PROPRIETORS:
City of Lincoln.

ESTABLISHED:
Planted 1973.

NUMBER OF VINES:
400.

THE WINE:
The vines were a gift from a group of wine enthusiasts in Lincoln's twin town of Neustadt, which is the centre of Germany's Palatinate region. The City's gardening staff care for the vineyard and the wine which is produced is used for civic functions in Lincoln.

NAME OF VINEYARD:
Little Pook Hill.

PROPRIETORS:
D. and J. Simmons.

ADDRESS:
Burwash Weald, Etchingham, East Sussex.

ESTABLISHED:
1973, 1974 and 1975.

AREA:
4·5 acres.

VINE VARIETIES:
Müller-Thurgau, Reichensteiner, Seyval Blanc and others.

HEIGHT ABOVE SEA LEVEL:
121 m (400 feet).

SOIL:
Loamy clay.

THE WINE:
Not yet in production.

VISITING ARRANGEMENTS:
Not open to the public.

NAME OF VINEYARD:
Longueville House.

PROPRIETOR:
Michael O'Callaghan.

ADDRESS:
Longueville, Mallow, County Cork, Irish Republic.

ESTABLISHED:
1972.

AREA:
3·5 acres.

VINE VARIETIES:
Müller-Thurgau, Reichensteiner.

THE WINE:
The wine from the Müller-Thurgau grapes was first made in 1977 and is available at the proprietor's country-house hotel in Longueville.

NAME OF VINEYARD:
Marriage Hill.

PROPRIETOR:
Michael Waterfield.

ADDRESS:
Marriage Farm, Wye, Ashford, Kent.

ESTABLISHED:
1972.

AREA:
1·5 acres.

NUMBER OF VINES:
2500.

VINE VARIETIES:
Müller-Thurgau, Scheurebe,
Reichensteiner.

HEIGHT ABOVE SEA LEVEL:
106 m (350 feet).

SOIL:
Chalky.

THE WINE:
The light and delicately flavoured
white wine is made in the estate
winery and is available at Browns
Kitchen Shop, Chilham, Kent, and at
the Wife of Bath Restaurant in Wye.

VISITING ARRANGEMENTS:
Not open to the public.

NAME OF VINEYARD:
The Martlet.

PROPRIETOR:
Mrs S. Monkton.

ADDRESS:
Stretton Hall, Stretton, Stafford.

ESTABLISHED:
1972.

VINE VARIETIES:
Müller-Thurgau, Seyve-Villard,
Reichensteiner.

HEIGHT ABOVE SEA LEVEL:
122 m (400 feet).

SOIL:
Medium heavy.

THE WINE:
The wine is made at Merrydown Wine
Company, and is available from the
vineyard.

VISITING ARRANGEMENTS:
Not open to the public, but it is
possible to make an appointment for
a private visit. Write to Mrs Monkton.

NAME OF VINEYARD:
Maryville Vineyard.

PROPRIETOR:
L. N. Weale.

ADDRESS:
Maryville House, Kilworth, Mallow,
County Cork, Irish Republic.

ESTABLISHED:
1972.

NUMBER OF VINES:
1700.

VINE VARIETIES:
Müller-Thurgau, Seyval Blanc,
Madeleine Sylvaner.

SOIL:
Sandy.

THE WINE:
The wine is made by Mr Weale on the
estate.

NAME OF VINEYARD:
Merton Grange.

PROPRIETORS:
Dr John Scott and Dr Anthony Ellis.

ADDRESS:
Station Road, Gamlingay, Sandy,
Bedfordshire.

ESTABLISHED:
Winter 1978.

AREA:
1·5 acres increasing to 13 acres.

NUMBER OF VINES:
1300 plus.

VINE VARIETIES:
Müller-Thurgau, Huxelrebe, Ortega,
Reichensteiner, Seibel.

HEIGHT ABOVE SEA LEVEL:
61 m (200 feet).

SOIL:
Loam/gravel.

THE WINE:
Not yet in production, will be made on
estate.

VISITING ARRANGEMENTS:
Not open to the public.

NAME OF VINEYARD:
Nash and Steyning.

PROPRIETORS:
Tim and Beth Parker.

ADDRESS:
19 The Cliff, Brighton, East Sussex.

ESTABLISHED:
1970 onwards.

AREA:
1 acre.

NUMBER OF VINES:
500.

VINE VARIETIES:
Müller-Thurgau, Ortega, Madeleine
Angevine, Seyve-Villard, Huxelrebe
and others.

HEIGHT ABOVE SEA LEVEL:
30 m (100 feet).

SOIL:
Sandy loam.

THE WINE:
Made by Merrydown Wine Company,
the wine is not available commercially.

VISITING ARRANGEMENTS:
Not open to the public.

NAME OF VINEYARD:
Nevards.

PROPRIETOR:
R. E. Barrett.

ADDRESS:
Boxted, Colchester, Essex.

ESTABLISHED:
1977.

AREA:
1 acre.

NUMBER OF VINES:
1480.

VINE VARIETIES:
Pinot Gris and a few Müller-Thurgau.

SOIL:
Light sandy loam.

THE WINE:
Not yet in production.

VISITING ARRANGEMENTS:
Not open to the public, but private
visits can be arranged with Mr Barrett.

NAME OF VINEYARD:
New Hall Vineyard.

PROPRIETOR:
S. W. Greenwood.

ADDRESS:
Purleigh, Chelmsford, Essex.

ESTABLISHED:
1970.

AREA:
18 acres.

NUMBER OF VINES:
18,000.

VINE VARIETIES:
Huxelrebe, Pinot Noir,
Müller-Thurgau, Perle, Reichensteiner.

HEIGHT ABOVE SEA LEVEL:
12 m (40 feet).

SOIL:
London clay.

THE WINE:
The range of wines is produced in the
estate winery and is obtainable from
the vineyard and also Merrydown Wine
Shop, Horam, East Sussex; Ley &
Wheeler, Colchester; and Kelvedon
Wine Agencies, Kelvedon, Essex.

VISITING ARRANGEMENTS:
Open one day each year at the end of
September or beginning of October;
details from the vineyard, telephone
Purleigh (062 185) 343.

NAME OF VINEYARD:
Newington Grounds.

PROPRIETORS:
Banbury Wine Ltd (W. B. C. Stapleton).

ADDRESS:
North Newington, Banbury, Oxon.

ESTABLISHED:
1977.

AREA:
3·5 acres.

NUMBER OF VINES:
3600.

VARIETIES:
Müller-Thurgau, Huxelrebe,
Reichensteiner.

HEIGHT ABOVE SEA LEVEL:
122 m (400 feet).

SOIL:
Clay loam.

THE WINE:
From 1979 three Banbury Cross wines
will be made from the varieties grown
and available from Banbury Wine Ltd.

VISITING ARRANGEMENTS:
Visits by appointment with Banbury
Wine Ltd.

NAME OF VINEYARD:
Old Shields.

PROPRIETOR:
A. E. Marshall.

ADDRESS:
Old Shields Farm, Ardleigh, Essex.

ESTABLISHED:
1971.

AREA:
2·5 acres.

NUMBER OF VINES:
2500.

VINE VARIETIES:
Müller-Thurgau, Pinot Gris.

HEIGHT ABOVE SEA LEVEL:
30 m (100 feet).

SOIL:
Loam over gravel.

THE WINE:
Old Shields wine is available from the
vineyard and is made at Merrydown
Wine Company.

VISITING ARRANGEMENTS:
Not open to the public, but visits
possible by prior arrangement with
Mr Marshall, telephone Colchester
(0206) 230251.

NAME OF VINEYARD:
Parsonage Fields.

PROPRIETOR:
J. H. Abbs.

ADDRESS:
'Old Thatch', Bistock, Doddington,
Sittingbourne, Kent.

ESTABLISHED:
1977–8.

AREA:
2 acres.

NUMBER OF VINES:
4000 initially.

VINE VARIETIES:
Müller-Thurgau, Ortega,
Reichensteiner.

HEIGHT ABOVE SEA LEVEL:
66 m (220 feet).

SOIL:
Loam over gravel clay on chalk.

THE WINE:
Not yet in production.

VISITING ARRANGEMENTS:
Not open to the public.

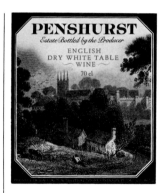

NAME OF VINEYARD:
Peasenhall.

PROPRIETORS:
R. and I. Macfarlane.

ADDRESS:
Elder Hall, Peasenhall, Saxmundham,
Suffolk.

ESTABLISHED:
1974.

AREA:
2 acres.

NUMBER OF VINES:
2600.

VARIETIES:
Müller-Thurgau.

HEIGHT ABOVE SEA LEVEL:
24 m (80 feet).

SOIL:
Clay loam, chalky.

THE WINE:
Made at Bruisyard Wines, Suffolk, the
wine is available from the vineyard and
M. Ramm, Bungay; Cherrybank
Estates, Otley and local pubs in Suffolk.

VISITING ARRANGEMENTS:
Not open to public.

NAME OF VINEYARD:
Penshurst.

PROPRIETORS:
W. H. and D. M. A. Westphal.

ADDRESS:
The Grove, Penshurst, Tonbridge,
Kent.

ESTABLISHED:
1972–5.

AREA:
3·25 acres.

NUMBER OF VINES:
3200.

VINE VARIETIES:
Müller-Thurgau, Reichensteiner.

HEIGHT ABOVE SEA LEVEL:
46 m (150 feet).

SOIL:
Loamy clay.

THE WINE:
Made at Lamberhurst Priory, the wine
is available from Penshurst Stores and
by the case from the vineyard.

VISITING ARRANGEMENTS:
Not open to public but visitors
welcome by prior arrangement.

NAME OF VINEYARD:
Pilton Manor.

PROPRIETOR:
Nigel de Marsac Godden.

ADDRESS:
Pilton, Shepton Mallet, Somerset.

ESTABLISHED:
1966–8.

AREA:
4·25 acres.

NUMBER OF VINES:
Over 8000.

VINE VARIETIES:
Müller-Thurgau, Seyval Blanc,
Huxelrebe; also small quantities of
eight other varieties.

HEIGHT ABOVE SEA LEVEL:
52 m (170 feet).

SOIL:
Stony topsoil overlying limestone, clay
and blue lias.

THE WINES:
A Riesling Sylvaner and Seyval Blanc
are made in the estate winery and are
available from the vineyard and also
Avery & Co. and Morans of Bristol
Ltd in Bristol; Harrods and the Ebury
Wine Co. in London; Eldridge
Pope & Co. Ltd, Dorchester; Tanners
Wines Ltd, Shrewsbury; Young &
Sanders, Edinburgh and the Merrydown
Wine Shop, Horam, East Sussex.

VISITING ARRANGEMENTS:
Private groups of twenty or more by
arrangement Monday to Friday after

NAME OF VINEYARD:
Polmassick.

PROPRIETORS:
Mr and Mrs P. J. Crowe.

ADDRESS:
Polmassick, St Ewe, St Austell,
Cornwall.

ESTABLISHED:
1976 onwards.

AREA:
1.5 acres; still expanding.

NUMBER OF VINES:
3000.

VINE VARIETIES:
Müller-Thurgau and Seyve-Villard.

HEIGHT ABOVE SEA LEVEL:
30–60 m (100–200 feet).
Heavy loam over shillet.

THE WINE:
Not yet in production but will be made
in the estate winery.

VISITING ARRANGEMENTS:
Open to public, details from the
vineyard.

17.00 mid June to 2 September.
Open to public Sundays from end
August to end September from 12.00
to 18.00. Buffet lunch and refreshments
available. For further details telephone:
Pilton (074 989) 325.

NAME OF VINEYARD:
Poulner Vineyard.

PROPRIETORS:
Mr and Mrs H. I. Bird.

ADDRESS:
Beech Knoll, Poulner Hill, Ringwood,
Hants.

ESTABLISHED:
1974, 1975 and 1976.

AREA:
1 acre.

NUMBER OF VINES:
820.

VINE VARIETIES:
Müller-Thurgau, Seyval, Leon Millot,
Zweigeltrebe.

HEIGHT ABOVE SEA LEVEL:
60 m (200 feet).

SOIL:
Clay and gravel.

THE WINE:
Not yet in commercial production.

VISITING ARRANGEMENTS:
Not open to the public.

NAME OF VINEYARD:
Pulham Vineyards Ltd.

PROPRIETORS:
Peter W. Cook and Arthur W. Cook.

ADDRESS:
Mill Lane, Pulham Market, Diss,
Norfolk.

ESTABLISHED:
1971, 1972, 1974 and 1976.

AREA:
6 acres.

NUMBER OF VINES:
12,000.

VINE VARIETIES:
Müller-Thurgau, Pinot Noir,
Auxerrois, Bacchus, Optima, Elbling.

SOIL:
Sandy loam.

THE WINES:
The vineyards are patterned on those of
the Upper Moselle region of
Luxembourg, and Germany. Winner of
Gore Brown Trophy, 1977 and Bronze
Medal, 1978.
Magdalen Rivaner is made in the
estate winery and is available in local
shops and restaurants and through
Lawrence Hayward Ltd, 11 Gough
Square, London EC4.

VISITING ARRANGEMENTS:
Tours of the vineyard and wine tasting
during August and September by
appointment only.

RENISHAW

WHITE WINE

Grown and bottled on the estate
by Reresby Sitwell
at Renishaw Hall near Sheffield

NAME OF VINEYARD:
Rake Manor.

ADDRESS:
Milford, Godalming, Surrey.

ESTABLISHED:
1974.

AREA:
1 acre.

NUMBER OF VINES:
1200.

VINE VARIETY:
Müller-Thurgau.

SOIL:
Light loam.

THE WINE:
The wine is made at the Merrydown
Wine Company.

VISITING ARRANGEMENTS:
Not open to the public.

NAME OF VINEYARD:
Renishaw.

PROPRIETOR:
Reresby Sitwell.

ADDRESS:
Renishaw Hall, Renishaw, Sheffield.
(Note: this is the postal address;
Renishaw Hall is actually in
Derbyshire).

ESTABLISHED:
1972 to 1975.

AREA:
2 acres.

NUMBER OF VINES:
2600.

VINE VARIETIES:
Seyval, Reichensteiner, Pinot Meunier
and others.

HEIGHT ABOVE SEA LEVEL:
60 m (200 feet).

SOIL:
Very fine sandy loam.

THE WINE:
Made in the estate winery.

VISITING ARRANGEMENTS:
Not open to the public but private
visits occasionally possible by prior
arrangement with estate office.

NAME OF VINEYARD:
Rock Lodge Vineyard.

PROPRIETOR:
Norman Cowderoy.

ADDRESS:
Scaynes Hill, Haywards Heath, West
Sussex.

ESTABLISHED:
1965 onwards.

AREA:
2 acres extending to 8 acres.

VINE VARIETIES:
Müller-Thurgau, Reichensteiner.

HEIGHT ABOVE SEA LEVEL:
61 m (200 feet).

SOIL:
Sandy loam over sandstone.

THE WINE:
Made in the estate winery and
available from the vineyard; Fortnum
& Mason Ltd, London; English Wine
Shops and other retail outlets.

VISITING ARRANGEMENTS:
Not open to the public but visits can
be arranged with the proprietor:
telephone Scaynes Hill (044 486) 224.

NAME OF VINEYARD:
The Saffron Walden Vineyard.

PROPRIETORS:
B. J. Hoar and Company.

ADDRESS:
Sewards End, Saffron Walden, Essex.

ESTABLISHED:
1977 onwards.

AREA:
2·5 acres.

NUMBER OF VINES:
2500.

VINE VARIETIES:
Müller-Thurgau, Chardonnay,
Huxelrebe.

HEIGHT ABOVE SEA LEVEL:
98 m (325 feet).

SOIL:
Silt loam over chalky boulder clay.

THE WINE:
Not yet in production.

VISITING ARRANGEMENTS:
Visits to the vineyard can be arranged
by contacting B. J. Hoar, telephone
Saffron Walden (0799) 27754.

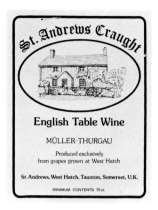

NAME OF VINEYARD:
St Andrews.

PROPRIETORS:
J. M. and R. G. Jenkins.

ADDRESS:
Virgins, West Hatch, Taunton,
Somerset.

ESTABLISHED:
1973.

AREA:
1 acre.

NUMBER OF VINES:
2000.

VINE VARIETIES:
Müller-Thurgau.

HEIGHT ABOVE SEA LEVEL:
45 m (150 feet).

SOIL:
Clay.

THE WINE:
The wine is made at Pilton Manor and
can be purchased from the vineyard.

VISITING ARRANGEMENTS:
Not open to the public.

NAME OF VINEYARD:
Shelsley Beauchamp Vineries.

PROPRIETOR:
J. Wilkinson.

ADDRESS:
Shelsley Beauchamp, Worcester.

ESTABLISHED:
1974–7; possibly extending further.

AREA:
1 acre, possibly extending by 3 acres.

NUMBER OF VINES:
600.

VINE VARIETIES:
Müller-Thurgau.

HEIGHT ABOVE SEA LEVEL:
150 m (500 feet).

SOIL:
Clay.

THE WINE:
Not yet in production.

VISITING ARRANGEMENTS:
Visits can be made to the vineyard,
telephone Shelsley Beauchamp
(088 65) 230 for appointment.

NAME OF VINEYARD:
Silver Green.

PROPRIETOR:
William Gurney.

ADDRESS:
Hempnall, Norfolk.

ESTABLISHED:
1974.

AREA:
1 ·5 acres.

NUMBER OF VINES:
2000.

VINE VARIETIES:
Müller-Thurgau.

HEIGHT ABOVE SEA LEVEL:
46 m (150 feet).

SOIL:
Clay boulder/chalk.

THE WINE:
Hemnall Müller-Thurgau is available by the case from the vineyard.

VISITING ARRANGEMENTS:
Not open to the public.

NAME OF VINEYARD:
Snipe Vineyards.

PROPRIETORS:
R. P. and J. I. Basham.

ADDRESS:
Snipe Cottage, Clopton, Woodbridge, Suffolk.

ESTABLISHED:
1977.

AREA:
2 acres.

NUMBER OF VINES:
2000.

VINE VARIETIES:
Müller-Thurgau.

SOIL:
Medium loam on heavy clay subsoil.

HEIGHT ABOVE SEA LEVEL:
46 m (150 feet).

THE WINE:
First production of Kingshall wine in 1979.

VISITING ARRANGEMENTS:
Not open to the public yet.

NAME OF VINEYARD:
Southcott.

PROPRIETOR:
Dr H. H. Crabb.

ADDRESS:
Pewsey, Wiltshire.

ESTABLISHED:
1973.

AREA:
1 acre.

NUMBER OF VINES:
1000.

VINE VARIETIES:
Müller-Thurgau, Septimer and Ortega.

HEIGHT ABOVE SEA LEVEL:
96 m (320 feet).

SOIL:
Greensand.

THE WINE:
The wine is made at Merrydown Wine
Company but not distributed
commercially.

VISITING ARRANGEMENTS:
The vineyard is not open to the public
and it is not possible to visit.

NAME OF VINEYARD:
Staple.

PROPRIETOR:
W. T. Ash.

ADDRESS:
Church Farm, Staple, Canterbury,
Kent.

ESTABLISHED:
1974–8.

AREA:
5·5 acres.

NUMBER OF VINES:
11,250.

VINE VARIETIES:
Müller-Thurgau, Huxelrebe.

HEIGHT ABOVE SEA LEVEL:
30 m (100 feet).

SOIL:
Rich top soil over chalk.

THE WINE:
Made in Biddenden Winery and
available from the vineyard.

VISITING ARRANGEMENTS:
Not open to public but arrangements to
visit can be made by writing to
proprietor.

NAME OF VINEYARD:
Stert.

PROPRIETORS:
Dr and Mrs G. L. Caldow.

ADDRESS:
Barn Cottage, Stert, Devizes, Wilts.

ESTABLISHED:
1975 to present.

AREA:
0·75 acre.

NUMBER OF VINES:
1200.

VINE VARIETIES:
Müller-Thurgau, Wrotham Pinot and fifteen experimental varieties.

HEIGHT ABOVE SEA LEVEL:
76–122 m (250–400 feet).

SOIL:
Fine loam over greensand.

THE WINE:
Made in Pilton Manor Winery and available from the vineyard.

VISITING ARRANGEMENTS:
Not open to public.

NAME OF VINEYARD:
Stocks Vineyard.

PROPRIETOR:
Mr R. M. O. Capper.

ADDRESS:
The Stocks Farm, Suckley, Worcester.

ESTABLISHED:
1972 and 1979.

AREA:
11 acres.

NUMBER OF VINES:
15,000.

VINE VARIETIES:
Müller-Thurgau.

HEIGHT ABOVE SEA LEVEL:
120 m (400 feet).

SOIL:
Heavy.

THE WINE:
The wine is made at Merrydown Wine Company and is available locally and from wine merchants.

VISITING ARRANGEMENTS:
Not open to the public but visits possible by appointment with Mr Capper.

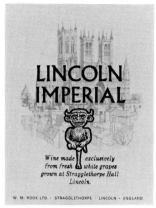

LINCOLN IMPERIAL

Wine made exclusively from fresh white grapes grown at Stragglethorpe Hall Lincoln.

W. M. ROOK LTD. · STRAGGLETHORPE · LINCOLN · ENGLAND

NAME OF VINEYARD:
Stragglethorpe.

PROPRIETOR:
Major A. Rook.

ADDRESS:
Stragglethorpe Hall, Stragglethorpe, Lincoln.

ESTABLISHED:
1964.

AREA:
2 acres.

NUMBER OF VINES:
4500.

VINE VARIETIES:
Seyval, Müller-Thurgau.

HEIGHT ABOVE SEA LEVEL:
13 m (44 feet).

SOIL:
Clay.

THE WINE:
Lincoln Imperial is made in estate winery and distributed by Skinner Rook and Chambers Ltd, 132 Church Street, Eastwood, Nottingham.

VISITING ARRANGEMENTS:
Not open to the public.

NAME OF VINEYARD:
Tenterden.

PROPRIETORS:
Spots Farm Ltd.

ADDRESS:
Spots Farm, Small Hythe, Tenterden, Kent.

ESTABLISHED:
1977.

AREA:
5 ·75 acres.

NUMBER OF VINES:
9300.

VINE VARIETIES:
Müller-Thurgau, 4000; Reichensteiner, 1250; Gutenborner, 1250; Seyval Blanc, 2000; and twenty-three experimental varieties.

HEIGHT ABOVE SEA LEVEL:
18 m (60 feet).

SOIL:
Tunbridge Wells/Ashdown sands.

THE WINE:
The wine will be made in the estate winery and be available from the vineyard shop.

VISITING ARRANGEMENTS:
Not open to public but private visits can be arranged; telephone Tenterden (058 06) 3033.

ENGLISH WHITE WINE PRODUCED FROM RIESLING-SYLVANER
GRAPES GROWN IN THE CASTLE GROUNDS.
Kenneth Bell   Min: contents. 70 cl.

NAME OF VINEYARD:
Thornbury Castle.

PROPRIETOR:
Kenneth Bell.

ADDRESS:
Thornbury Castle, Bristol.

ESTABLISHED:
1972.

AREA:
1 acre.

NUMBER OF VINES:
2000.

VINE VARIETIES:
Müller-Thurgau.

HEIGHT ABOVE SEA LEVEL:
15 m (50 feet).

THE WINE:
Made on the estate and available at
the Thornbury Castle restaurant.

VISITING ARRANGEMENTS:
Not open to the public.

NAME OF VINEYARD:
Three Choirs.

PROPRIETOR:
A. A. McKechnie.

ADDRESS:
Fairfields Fruit Farm Ltd, Rhyle
House, Newent, Gloucestershire.

ESTABLISHED:
1973, 1974 and 1977.

AREA:
6 acres.

VINE VARIETIES:
Müller-Thurgau and Reichensteiner.

HEIGHT ABOVE SEA LEVEL:
60 m (200 feet).

SOIL:
Sandy loam.

THE WINE:
The wine is made on the estate and is
available at many hotels and restaurants
in the West Midlands, and also from
Vines Stores, Ledbury and the Old
Customs House, The Quay,
Gloucester.

VISITING ARRANGEMENTS:
Not open to the public, but group
visits can be arranged with Mr T. Day
at the vineyard, telephone
Dymock (053 185) 223.

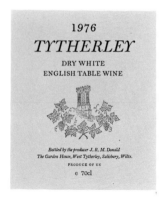

NAME OF VINEYARD:
Tytherley.

PROPRIETOR:
J. R. M. Donald.

ADDRESS:
The Garden House, West Tytherley,
Salisbury, Wiltshire.

ESTABLISHED:
1970–3.

VINE VARIETIES:
Müller-Thurgau and some experimental
varieties.

HEIGHT ABOVE SEA LEVEL:
61 m (200 feet).

SOIL:
Gravel, clay, loam above chalk.

THE WINE:
Made on the estate and available from
the vineyard.

VISITING ARRANGEMENTS:
Not open to public except for sale of
wine, but occasional visits possible
by appointment; telephone
Lockerley (0794) 40644.

NAME OF VINEYARD:
Valley Wine Cellars.

PROPRIETOR:
Christopher Ann.

MANAGER:
David Allcorn.

ADDRESS:
English Wine Centre, Alfriston,
Polegate, East Sussex.

ESTABLISHED:
1970.

AREA:
0·5 acre.

VINE VARIETIES:
Müller-Thurgau and others.

THE WINE:
Cuckmere wine, 'light, dry but fruity',
is available from the Valley Wine
Cellars.

ARRANGEMENTS FOR VISITING:
The cellars are open most days and
visitors are welcome, although it is
advisable to telephone first to ensure
someone is there. Group visits to the
vineyard, cellars and museum can be
arranged with the manager; telephone
Alfriston (0323) 870532. The wine
cellar sells a hundred English wines and
the museum has 150-year-old press,
antique corkscrews, wine bottles and
vineyard paraphernalia from the past
four hundred years.

NAME OF VINEYARD:
Wenden.

PROPRIETORS:
Ronald and Joyce Jeffries.

ADDRESS:
Duddenhoe End, Saffron Walden,
Essex.

ESTABLISHED:
1972–3.

AREA:
3 acres.

NUMBER OF VINES:
5000.

VINE VARIETIES:
Müller-Thurgau.

HEIGHT ABOVE SEA LEVEL:
122 m (400 feet).

SOIL:
Boulder clay on chalk.

THE WINE:
Made at the Chilford Hundred Winery,
the dry white wine is available from the
vineyard and Peatling & Cawdron,
Bury St Edmunds, Suffolk, and
branches in the region.

VISITING ARRANGEMENTS:
Not open to public, but visits can be
arranged; telephone:
Chrishall (076 383) 484.

NAME OF VINEYARD:
Wern Dêg.

PROPRIETOR:
Dr G. I. Thomas.

ADDRESS:
Llanarth, Dyfed, Wales.

ESTABLISHED:
1964.

AREA:
4 acres.

WINE VARIETIES:
Seyval Blanc, Müller-Thurgau,
Chardonnay, Ortega, Perle,
Reichensteiner.

HEIGHT ABOVE SEA LEVEL:
122 m (200 feet).

SOIL:
Clay.

THE WINE:
Made at the Merrydown Wine
Company in Sussex, the medium dry
wine is available at local hotels and
restaurants.

VISITING ARRANGEMENTS:
Not open to the public.

NAME OF VINEYARD:
Westbury.

PROPRIETOR:
B. H. Theobald.

ADDRESS:
Westbury Farm, Purley, Reading,
Berkshire.

ESTABLISHED:
1973–8.

AREA:
15 acres.

NUMBER OF VINES:
About 7000 (410 per acre).

VINE VARIETIES:
Twenty-eight French and German
varieties, both red and white.

HEIGHT ABOVE SEA LEVEL:
38 m (125 feet).

SOIL:
Loam over gravel.

THE WINE:
Four white and two red wines are made
in the estate winery and may be
purchased from the vineyard.

VISITING ARRANGEMENTS:
Parties of twenty or more by prior
arrangement. For tour of the vineyard
(or in winter a slide show) plus lecture
and wine tasting telephone proprietor:
Pangbourne (073 57) 3123.

NAME OF VINEYARD:
Wetheringsett.

PROPRIETOR:
K. Bolton.

ADDRESS:
Green Farm, Wetheringsett,
Stowmarket, Suffolk.

AREA:
1 acre.

THE WINE:
Wine not for sale.

VISITING ARRANGEMENTS:
Vineyard not open to visitors.

NAME OF VINEYARD:
Whitstone Vineyards.

PROPRIETORS:
Laura and George Barclay.

ADDRESS:
Whitstone House, Bovey Tracey,
Newton Abbot, Devon.

ESTABLISHED:
1974 and 1978.

AREA:
1 ·5 acres.

NUMBER OF VINES:
1000.

VINE VARIETIES:
Müller-Thurgau, Madeleine Angevine.

HEIGHT ABOVE SEA LEVEL:
75 m (350 feet).

SOIL:
Rocky.

NAME OF VINEYARD:
Whittington.

PROPRIETORS:
Roger White and David Brockington.

ADDRESS:
c/o 14 Frederick Place, Clifton,
Bristol 8. The vineyard is situated on
the edge of the Mendips.

ESTABLISHED:
1976.

AREA:
0 ·5 acre increasing to 2 acres.

NUMBER OF VINES:
550.

VINE VARIETIES:
Müller-Thurgau, Madeleine Angevine.

HEIGHT ABOVE SEA LEVEL:
107 m (350 feet).

SOIL:
Loam.

THE WINE:
The wine is produced at the vineyard
and is not yet for sale.

VISITING ARRANGEMENTS:
The vineyard is one of the schemes
linked with the experimental school the
proprietors run in Bristol. It is not open
to the public, but it is possible to
arrange private visits, telephone
Bristol (0272) 311995 or 291774.

NAME OF VINEYARD:
Woburn.

PROPRIETOR:
Woburn Vineyard (Raymond Lescott).

ADDRESS:
Aspley Lane, Woburn, Beds.

ESTABLISHED:
1978.

AREA:
3·5 acres.

NUMBER OF VINES:
5078.

VINE VARIETIES:
Müller-Thurgau and others.

HEIGHT ABOVE SEA LEVEL:
About 107 m (350 feet).

SOIL:
Sandy loam.

THE WINE:
Will be made by Merrydown Wine
Company and will be available from
Woburn Abbey, local outlets and
Anthony Beccle, Wine Shipper; or
from the vineyard.

VISITING ARRANGEMENTS:
Not open to the public but visits can be
arranged with the proprietor.

NAME OF VINEYARD:
Woodfarm Vineyard.

PROPRIETORS:
Don and Deidre Shepherd.

ADDRESS:
Fressingfield, Diss, Norfolk.

ESTABLISHED:
1972–3.

AREA:
3·5 acres.

NUMBER OF VINES:
4000.

VINE VARIETIES:
Müller-Thurgau with some Pinot Gris
and Pinot Noir.

HEIGHT ABOVE SEA LEVEL:
48 m (160 feet).

SOIL:
Sandy clay loam.

THE WINE:
Dry white Fressingfield wine is made
from Müller-Thurgau grapes at Anglia
Vineyards in Bruisyard. It is available
from the vineyard and from Carley &
Webb, Framlingham, White Horse Inn,
Badingham and others locally.

VISITING ARRANGEMENTS:
Private visits may be possible.
This vineyard will be of interest to
disabled people as Mr Shepherd is
disabled and it was planted with this in
mind. The equipment has been adapted
in order that he can tend the vineyard.
Telephone Fressingfield (037 986) 223.

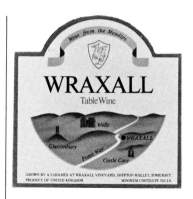

NAME OF VINEYARD:
Wootton Vines.

PROPRIETORS:
Major and Mrs C. L. B. Gillespie.

ADDRESS:
North Wootton, Shepton Mallet,
Somerset.

ESTABLISHED:
1971, 1973 and 1978.

AREA:
5 acres.

NUMBER OF VINES:
8500.

VINE VARIETIES:
Müller-Thurgau, Schönburger,
Seyval, Auxerrois.

HEIGHT ABOVE SEA LEVEL:
21 m (70 feet).

SOIL:
Medium loam.

THE WINE
Made on the estate, the wines are
available from David Baillie Vintners,
Exeter; in London at Findlater, Mackie,
Todd & Co. Ltd, 92 Wigmore Street,
W1, Bow Wine Vaults Ltd, 10 Bow
Churchyard, EC4; Whitesides of
Clitheroe, Lancs; and from the
vineyard.

VISITING ARRANGEMENTS:
The vineyard is open 14.00 to 17.00
daily except Tuesdays and Sundays.
The winery is open for organized tours
by groups of twenty-five people.

NAME OF VINEYARD:
Wraxall.

PROPRIETORS:
A. S. Holmes and Partners.

ADDRESS:
Wraxall Vineyard, Shepton Mallet,
Somerset.

ESTABLISHED:
1974–8.

AREA:
6 acres.

NUMBER OF VINES:
2400.

VINE VARIETIES:
Müller-Thurgau, Seyval Blanc,
Madeleine Angevine, Madeleine
Sylvaner, Gewürztraminer, and
thirty other experimental.

HEIGHT ABOVE SEA LEVEL:
61 m (200 feet).

SOIL:
Middle lias.

THE WINE:
The vineyard is run on the Geneva
Double Curtain system. The wine, a
blend of Müller-Thurgau and Seyval
Blanc, is made at Pilton Manor
Vineyard (*q.v.*) and is available from
the vineyard, and from Howells of
Bristol Ltd.

VISITING ARRANGEMENTS:
Not open to public but visits can be
made by prior arrangement with
owners.

NAME OF VINEYARD:
Yearlstone.

PROPRIETOR:
Miss Gillian Pearkes.

ADDRESS:
Yearlstone House, Bickleigh, Tiverton, Devon.

ESTABLISHED:
1976.

AREA:
1 ·5 acres expanding.

NUMBER OF VINES:
3000 plus.

VINE VARIETIES:
Siegerrebe, Chardonnay, Madeleine Angevine, a selection of red grape vines and a trial area of a hundred varieties.

HEIGHT ABOVE SEA LEVEL:
60 m (200 feet).

SOIL:
Red Devon loam on sandstone.

THE WINE:
The wine will be made on the estate and will be available from 1980 from the vineyard.

VISITING ARRANGEMENTS:
Parties and individuals welcome on open days; telephone Bickleigh (088 45) 450 for details. Occasional private visits, by appointment with Miss Pearkes.

🌺 *Vineyards to Visit*

BEDFORDSHIRE

Woburn, Aspley Lane, Woburn (Mr R. Lescott)
  By appointment only; Telephone Milton Keynes (0908) 582328.

BERKSHIRE

Kirby, Kirby Farm, Inkpen, Newbury (Hon. John Astor)
  Occasional, by appointment only. Enquiries to Kirby Farm Office.
Westbury, Westbury Farm, Purley, Reading (Mr B. H. Theobald)
  Parties of at least twenty, by appointment only, all year round (winter
  slide show) includes wine-tastings and lecture. Moderate charge.
  Telephone Pangbourne (073 57) 3123.

CAMBRIDGESHIRE

Gamlingay, Drove Road, Gamlingay (Post town: Sandy, Beds)
(G. P. and N. Reece)
  Group tours of thirty to fifty people by appointment only. Small charge
  includes wine-tasting. Telephone Gamlingay (0767) 50795.
Isle of Ely Vineyard, Wilburton, Ely (Mr Norman Sneesby)
  Spring and summer—group visits by appointment only, lecture tour
  and tastings.

CHANNEL ISLANDS

La Mare, Elms Farm, St Mary, Jersey (R. H. and A. M. Blayley)
  Open to public from mid-May to end September, Monday to Friday.
  No set tour but visitors can follow a numbered trail at their leisure and
  see vineyard, winery and press house. Building of historic interest and
  special adventure playground for children. Nominal charge.
  Vineyard shop.

CORNWALL

Polmassick, Mellyn Boyse, Polmassick, St Ewe, St Austell
(Mr and Mrs P. J. Crowe)
  Write to proprietors for details.

DERBYSHIRE

Renishaw Hall, Renishaw (Post town: Sheffield) (Mr Reresby Sitwell)
  Visits by arrangement only. Write to owner or to estate office. Wines
  not for sale.

DEVON

Clyston, Broadclyst, Exeter (A. E. Forbes, P. J. Hunt, P. B. Miles,
C. C. G. Trump)
  Groups of twenty to thirty people by written arrangement only.

ESSEX

The Vineyard, Crown Lane, Ardleigh, Colchester (C. E. and R. E. George)
  By appointment only with proprietors.
Felstar, The Vineyards, Cricks Green, Felsted, Dunmow
(J. G. and I. M. Barrett)
  Conducted group visits at weekends only, by appointment. Shop open
  all weekdays and it is possible to look over the vineyard alone.
  Telephone Great Leighs (024 534) 504.
Fyfield Hall, Ongar (Mr R. J. White)
  Vineyard not yet selling wine but visitors by arrangement only with
  Mr White.
New Hall, Purleigh, Chelmsford (Mr S. W. Greenwood)
  One open day each year—end September or early October. Can be
  seen at other times by appointment with Mr Greenwood.
Wenden Vineyard, Duddenhoe End, Saffron Walden (R. and J. Jeffries)
  By appointment only. Telephone Chrishall (076 383) 484.

HAMPSHIRE

Beaulieu Abbey, Brockenhurst (Montagu Ventures Ltd)
  Organized parties by prior arrangement with: The Special Functions
  Organizer, John Montagu Building, Beaulieu, Brockenhurst.
Hambledon Vineyard, Mill Down, Hambledon, Portsmouth (Sir Guy and
Lady Salisbury-Jones)
  Sunday afternoons end July to end September. Open day on August
  Bank Holiday. Visits on other days for public and private groups,
  small charge. Telephone Hambledon (070 132) 475. Refreshment room
  and good parking.

HEREFORD AND WORCESTER

Shelsley Beauchamp, Shelsley Grange, Shelsley Beauchamp, Worcester
(Mr J. Wilkinson)
  Not open to the public, but private visits can be arranged with the
  proprietor. Telephone Shelsley Beauchamp (088 65) 230.

HERTFORDSHIRE

Frithsden, Berkhamsted (Peter and Anne Latchford)
  Not open to public but weekend tours arranged. Write to Mr and
  Mrs Latchford, 38 Crouchfield, Hemel Hempstead.

IRELAND

Ballygagin, Dungarvan, Co. Waterford (An Foras Talúntais)
  Experimental vineyard run by Irish research organization. Visits by
  appointment only with An Foras Talúntais, Sandymount Avenue,
  Dublin 4.

ISLE OF WIGHT

Cranmore Vineyard, Cranmore Avenue, Yarmouth (R. H. Gibbons and
N. Poulter)
  Guided tours at a set time each week during August and September
  including wine-tasting. Details from proprietors. Parties of ten or more
  accepted at other times by arrangement only.

KENT

Biddenden Vineyard, Little Whatmans, Biddenden, Ashford
(Mr R. A. Barnes)
  Wine shop open daily (Sunday from noon, April to October only).
  Group visits of twenty-five to fifty people in July, August and
  September by arrangement only. Telephone Biddenden (0580) 291237.
Kentish Vineyards, Cherry Hill, Nettlestead, Maidstone (L. T. Bates and
G. Watson)
  Guided tours for parties of up to fifty people during July, August and
  September. Small charge. By appointment only.
Lamberhurst Priory Vineyards, Priory Farm, Lamberhurst, Tunbridge Wells
(K. McAlpine)
  Tours during summer months. Telephone Lamberhurst (089 278) 286.
Penshurst Vineyard, The Grove, Penshurst (Mr R. Westphal)
  By prior arrangement with the vineyard.
Staple Vineyards, Church Farm, Staple, Canterbury (W. T. Ash)
  By private arrangement with the owner.
Tenterden Vineyard, Spots Farm, Small Hythe, Tenterden (Spots Farm Ltd)
  By appointment only. Telephone Tenterden (058 06) 3033.

NORFOLK

Elmham Park, North Elmham, Dereham (Mr R. S. Don)
  Visits by arrangement only with Mr A. Bell at the vineyard.
Harling, Eastfield House, East Harling, Norwich (Mr and Mrs J. K.
Miljkovic)
  Visitors welcome by appointment only.

Heywood, Holly Farm, The Heywood, Diss (Mr and Mrs Aikman)
    By appointment only at weekends April to October. Telephone
    Diss (0379) 2461. This vineyard not yet in production; planted 1977.
Lexham Hall, King's Lynn (W. R. B. Foster and Partners)
    Parties by appointment only.
Pulham, Mill Lane, Pulham Market, Diss (P. W. and A. W. Cook)
    Tours by appointment only in August and September.
Woodfarm Vineyard, Fressingfield, Diss, Norfolk (Don and Deidre Shepherd)
    Not open to the public but private visits can be arranged. Of
    particular interest to disabled people—this vineyard has been
    established with this in mind and machinery etc. specially adapted.
    Telephone Fressingfield (037 986) 223.

OXFORDSHIRE

Newington Grounds, North Newington, Banbury (Banbury Wine Co. Ltd)
    By appointment with proprietor, Mr W. B. C. Stapleton.

SOMERSET

Brympton d'Evercy, Yeovil (Charles Clive-Ponsonby-Fane)
    Open from 1 May to end September, every day except Thursday and
    Friday. Staterooms, gardens, cider museum, vineyard etc. Further
    details obtainable from Brympton Estate Office, Yeovil.
Pilton Manor, Pilton, Shepton Mallet (Nigel de Marsac Godden)
    Public open days: Sundays end August to end September. Groups,
    minimum twenty, after 17.00 mid June to end September.
    Telephone Pilton (074 989) 325.
Wootton Vines, North Wootton, Shepton Mallet (Major and
Mrs C. L. B. Gillespie)
    Vineyard open for walking 14.00 to 17.00 daily except Tuesdays and
    Sundays. Visits to winery by appointment for twenty-five people per
    tour.
Wraxall, Shepton Mallet (A. S. Holmes and Partners)
    By appointment only, write to owners. Geneva Double Curtain system.

SUFFOLK

Anglia Vineyards Ltd, Broadwater, Framlingham, Woodbridge
(Mr and Mrs C. Knowles, Mr and Mrs R. Knowles, Mr and Mrs. I.
Berwick)
    By appointment only, groups of ten to fifty-three people 1 August to
    early October. Tour of vineyard, winery and wine-tasting.
Barningham Hall, Barningham, Bury St Edmunds (Mr M Hope)
    By appointment only during summer weekends. Telephone Mrs E. R.

Hope, Coney Weston (035 921) 498.
Cavendish Manor, Nether Hall, Cavendish, Sudbury (Mr B. T. Ambrose)
 Open daily 11.00 to 16.00. Group visits by appointment. Picnic site,
 period house, Constable paintings, lovely countryside.
Finn Valley, Cherrybank Estates, Otley, Ipswich (Mr C. Clark)
 Parties by appointment. One or two open weekends per year—
 advertised in local press.
Genesis Green Vineyard, Wickhambrook, Newmarket (Fuller Roope
Partnership: M. H. C. Fuller, Major and Mrs F. Fuller)
 Parties of not less than fifteen by prior arrangement only with the
 management.
Henny Vineyard, The Old Rectory, Little Henny, Sudbury (S. R. Copley)
 Nothing organized but visits possible by appointment with proprietor.
Kelsale Vineyard, The Manor Farm House, The Street, Saxmundham
(Mr J. T. Edgerley)
 By arrangement only, write or telephone proprietor.
 Telephone Saxmundham (0728) 2043.

SURREY

Hascombe, Godalming (Lt-Cdr T. P. Baillie-Grohman)
Courses on viticulture etc. Visits by appointment only.
 Telephone Hascombe (048 632) 343.
Royal Horticultural Society, Wisley, Woking
 Open to the public. Two small vineyards in the Garden.

SUSSEX, EAST

Brede, Broad Oak, Rye (Mr R. D. Thorley)
 Visits by appointment only.
Flexerne, Fletching Common, Newick, Lewes (Mr and Mrs Roy Smith)
 By appointment with proprietors only. Telephone
 Newick (082 572) 2548.
Horam Manor, Horam, Heathfield (Merrydown Wine Company Ltd)
 Mondays to Fridays only, conducted tours; small charge includes guide
 and wine-tasting. Telephone Horam Road (04353) 2401 for details.
T. B. L. Parker, 19 The Cliff, Roedean, Brighton
 By appointment with proprietor.
Valley Wine Cellars, Drusillas Corner, Alfriston, Polegate (Mr C. M. D. Ann)
 Small vineyard restaurant, 300. Parties catered for. Telephone
 Alfriston (0323) 870532.
Westfield Vineyard, Yew Tree Farm, Hastings (Mr D. Carr Taylor)
 Visits most weekends during summer months, also by prior arrangement
 with owner, Geneva Double Curtain system.

SUSSEX, WEST

Arundel Vineyard, Arundel (Mr H. B. Evans)
  For details write to owner at Maltravers House, Maltravers Street,
  Arundel.
Chilsdown, The Old Station House, Singleton, Chichester (Ian and
Andrew Paget)
  Parties of twenty and over by arrangement. June to September a tour
  every evening at 17.15 Monday to Friday lasting about one hour. Also
  Saturdays in August and September. Open day August Bank Holiday
  from 14.00 to 16.00. Not Sundays. Telephone Singleton (024 363) 398.
Rock Lodge, Scaynes Hill, Haywards Heath (N. C. Cowderoy)
By appointment only. Telephone Scaynes Hill (044 486) 224.

WARWICKSHIRE

Cookhill, 'Crantock', 34 Oak Tree Lane, Cookhill, Alcaster
  Wine not for sale but visitors can see the vineyard by appointment only.
Telephone Astwood Bank (052 789) 2933.

WILTSHIRE

Aeshton Manor, Church Farm, Ashton Keynes, Swindon (Mr C. Stuart)
  Visits by arrangement only during late August and September. Write to
  Mr Stuart.
Tytherley, The Garden House, West Tytherley, Salisbury
(Mr J. R. M. Donald)
  Only open to the public for the purchase of wine, but occasional visits
  possible by arrangement with owner. Telephone Lockerley (0794) 40644.

APPENDIX SIX

🌿 *Winemaking Services*

BERKSHIRE

Mr B. H. Theobald, Westbury Farm, Purley, Reading.
CAMBRIDGESHIRE
S. Alper, Chilford Hundred, Chilford Hall, Linton, Cambridge.
G. P. and N. Reece, Gamlingay Vineyard, Drove Road, Gamlingay, Sandy, Beds.

GLOUCESTERSHIRE

Three Choirs Vineyard, Fairfields Farm, Rhyle House, Newent.

KENT

R. A. Barnes, Biddenden Vineyards, Little Whatmans, Biddenden, Ashford.
Lamberhurst Vineyards, Priory Farm, Lamberhurst, Tunbridge Wells.

NORFOLK

Mr R. S. Don, Elmham Park Vineyard, North Elmham, Dereham.
Mr P. and Mr A. Cook, Pulham Vineyard, Mill Lane, Pulham Market, Diss.

SOMERSET

Mr N. de M. Godden, Pilton Manor Vineyard, Shepton Mallet.
Major C. L. B. Gillespie, Wootton Vines, North Wootton, Shepton Mallet.

SUFFOLK

Anglia Vineyards Ltd, Broadwater, Framlingham. (Commercial quantities only.)
Finn Valley Vineyard, Cherrybank Estates, Otley, Ipswich.

SUSSEX

Merrydown Wine Company, Horam, Heathfield, East Sussex. (Cooperative scheme.)

WILTSHIRE

J. R. M. Donald, Tytherley Vineyard, The Garden House, West Tytherley, Salisbury.

❧ *Suppliers of Vines*

AVON

Roger White and David Brockington, Whittington Vineyard, c/o 14 Frederick Place, Bristol 8.

BEDFORDSHIRE

Woburn Vineyards, Aspley Lane, Woburn. (Post town: Milton Keynes, Bucks.)

BERKSHIRE

Bowden Vineyard, Lower Bowden Farm, Pangbourne, Reading.
Westbury Farm Vineyard, Purley Reading.

CAMBRIDGESHIRE

Gamlingay Vineyard, Drove Road, Gamlingay. (Post town: Sandy, Beds.)
The Isle of Ely Vineyard, Wilburton, Ely.

DEVON

Clyston Vineyard, Burrow Farm, Broadclyst, Exeter.
Yearlstone Vineyard, Yearlstone House, Bickleigh, Tiverton.

ESSEX

Boyton Vineyards, Hill Farm, Boyton End, Halstead, Essex.
Erdelega Vineyard, Orchard Meadow, Harts Lane, Ardleigh, Colchester.
Felstar, The Vineyards, Cricks Green, Felsted, Dunmow.
Ken Muir Berried Fruit Specialist, Honey Pot Farm, Weeley Heath, Clacton-on-Sea.

HEREFORD AND WORCESTER

Broadfield, Broadfield Court Estate, Bodenham, Hereford.
M. Jefferson-Brown, Maylite, Martley, Worcester. (Will supply by mail order.)
Shelsley Beauchamp Vineries, Shelsley Grange, Shelsley Beauchamp, Worcester.

HERTFORDSHIRE

Frithsden Vineyard, c/o Peter and Anne Latchford, 38 Crouchfield, Hemel Hempstead.
Mr G. Ordish, 178 London Road, St Albans.

ISLE OF WIGHT

Cranmore Vineyard, Cranmore Avenue, Yarmouth. (Will supply by mail order.)

KENT

Kentish Vineyards, Cherry Hill, Nettlestead, Maidstone.
Lamberhurst Priory Vineyards, Ridge Farm, Lamberhurst, Tunbridge Wells.
Penshurst Vineyard, The Grove, Penshurst.
Tenterden Vineyards, Spots Farm, Small Hythe, Tenterden.

MERSEYSIDE

S. E. Lytle & Co., Park Road Nurseries, Formby, Liverpool. (Will supply by mail order.)

NORFOLK

Elmham Park, North Elmham, Dereham.
Harling Vineyards, Eastfield House, East Harling, Norwich.
Heywood Vineyard, Holly Farm, The Heywood, Diss.
Wood Farm Vineyard, Wood Farm, Wicklewood, Wymondham.

OXFORDSHIRE

Hendred Vineyards, Corner House, Allins Lane, East Hendred, Wantage.
Newington Grounds Vineyard, North Newington, Banbury.

SOMERSET

Brympton d'Evercy Vineyard, Brympton d'Evercy, Yeovil.
Cufic Vines, Tuttors Hill, Cheddar.
Pilton Manor Vineyard, Shepton Mallet.
St Andrews, Virgins, West Hatch, Taunton.
Wootton Vines, North Wootton, Shepton Mallet.

STAFFORDSHIRE

The Martlet, Stretton Hall, Stretton, Stafford.

SUFFOLK

Anglia Vineyards Ltd, Broadwater, Framlingham, Woodbridge.
Barningham Hall, Barningham, Bury St Edmunds.
Cavendish Manor Vineyards, Nether Hall Manor, Cavendish, Sudbury.
Finn Valley Vineyard, Cherrybank Estates, Otley, Ipswich.
Grunsburg Vineyard, 34 Grundisburgh Road, Woodbridge.
Tongs Lane Nurseries, Cratfield, Halesworth. (Will supply by mail order.)

SURREY

Hoe Vineyard, Hoe House, Francis Field, Peaslake, Guildford.
Jackmans Nurseries Ltd, Egley Road, Woking. (Will supply by mail order.)
Royal Horticultural Society, Wisley, Woking.

SUSSEX, EAST

Breaky Bottom Vineyard, Rodmell, Lewes.
The Downland Vine Co., 19 The Cliff, Roedean, Brighton.
Flexerne Vineyard, Fletching Common, Newick.
Merrydown Wine Company, Horam, Heathfield. (Will supply by mail order.)
Westfield Vineyard, Yew Tree Farm, Wheel Lane, Westfield, Hastings.

SUSSEX, WEST

Arundel Vineyard, Maltravers House, Maltravers Street, Arundel.
Chilsdown Vineyard, Old Station House, Singleton, Chichester.

WALES

Wern Dêg Vineyard, Llanarth, Dyfed.

WARWICKSHIRE

Cookhill Vineyard, 34 Oak Tree Lane, Cookhill, Alcester.

WEST MIDLANDS

Selly Park Vineyard, 30 Upland Road, Selly Park, Birmingham.

WILTSHIRE

Tytherley Vineyard, The Garden House, West Tytherley, Salisbury.

❧ *Typical Price Structure for an English Wine*

Retail price £2.50 per bottle including 15 per cent VAT.

	Price per case of 12 bottles excluding VAT £	*Terms*	*Gross profit*		
1. *Under bond*					
Collected from winery					
To the UK trade	13.95	Cash within 28 days of invoice date			
Export	15.70	Cash within 40 days of invoice date			
Delivered		Cash within 28 days of invoice date			
1–5 cases	17.51				
6–14 cases	14.79				
15 or more cases	14.54				
2. *Duty paid*					
Delivered to wine merchant (wholesaler)		Cash within 28 days			
1–5 cases	23.61	of invoice date.	15%		
6–14 cases	20.84	Collection allowance		25%	
15 or more cases	20.55	50p per case			26%
Delivered to off-licences, licensed grocers, etc.	23.61			15%	
Delivered to hotels and restaurants	25.83 (=£2.15 per bottle)				
Retail price	£27.78 (=£2.31½ per bottle)				

Farm-gate sales from the winery should be made at full retail price but with a discount of, say, £1 per case for unbroken cases.

At the bottom of the table is the retail price. The vineyard receives all of this only by sale direct to the public at the vineyard gate or through direct mail.

A restaurant expects to buy at less than the price the public pays and then traditionally marks up 100%.

Off licences, including the village shop, will buy little but usually only expect to make 15 per cent on the selling price.

A wine merchant, who may act as a wholesaler, should buy in quantity and this is reflected in the price options offered.

Part 1 of the table shows prices at which a merchant with his own bonding facilities will buy under bond; and the price for export sales made on an 'under bond collected' basis.

The final method, not shown on the table, is to sell to an agent who will expect to buy at 10 to 15 per cent below wholesale prices and may demand exclusivity.

(Information in this appendix was kindly supplied by Mr Robin Don.)

❧ *Ministry of Agriculture, Fisheries and Food and the Welsh Office, Agriculture Department*

Divisional Offices in Areas Suitable for Viticulture

EASTERN REGION

Southgate, Bury St Edmunds, Suffolk (covering Suffolk); telephone Bury St Edmunds (0284) 3271.

Beeches Road, Chelmsford, Essex (covering Essex, Hertfordshire and parts of Greater London); telephone Chelmsford (0245) 53201.

Chequers Court, Huntingdon (covering Bedfordshire and Cambridgeshire); telephone Huntingdon (0480) 52161.

122A *Thorpe Road*, Norwich (covering Norfolk); telephone Norwich (0603) 29881.

EAST MIDLAND REGION

Block 7, Chalfont Drive, Nottingham (covering Derbyshire and Nottinghamshire); telephone Nottingham (0602) 291191.

Ceres House, 2 Searby Road, Lincoln (covering Lincolnshire); telephone Lincoln (0522) 29951.

Government Buildings, Gladstone Road, Northampton (covering Leicestershire and Northampton); telephone Northampton (0604) 52388.

SOUTH-WESTERN REGION

Alphington Road, Exeter, Devon (covering Devon); telephone Exeter (0392) 77951.

Elmbridge Court, Gloucester (covering Gloucestershire and Wiltshire); telephone Gloucester (0452) 21421.

Quantock House, Paul Street, Taunton, Somerset (covering Dorset and Somerset); telephone Taunton (0823) 87922.

Agar Road, Truro, Cornwall (covering Cornwall); telephone Truro (0872) 3191.

SOUTH-EASTERN REGION

Uplands, Epsom Road, Guildford, Surrey (covering Surrey, East and West Sussex and parts of Greater London); telephone Guildford (0483) 62881.

Crown House, Sittingbourne Road, Maidstone, Kent (covering Kent and parts of Greater London); telephone Maidstone (0622) 54300.

Government Buildings, Marston Road, New Marston, Oxford (covering Berkshire, Buckinghamshire and Oxfordshire); telephone Oxford (0865) 44891.

Government Buildings, Cromwell House, Andover Road, Winchester, Hants (covering Hampshire and the Isle of Wight); telephone Winchester (0962) 63500.

WEST MIDLAND REGION

Berkeley Towers, Crewe, Cheshire (covering Cheshire and Staffordshire); telephone Crewe (0270) 69211.

Whitehall, Monkmoor Road, Shrewsbury, Salop (covering Salop); telephone Shrewsbury (0743) 53961.

Government Buildings, Block C, Whittington Road, Worcester (covering Warwickshire, West Midland Metropolitan County and Hereford and Worcester); telephone Worcester (0905) 355355.

WALES

Crown Buildings, Penrallt, Caernarfon, Gwynedd (covering Gwynedd); telephone Caernarfon (0286) 4144.

Block 2, Government Buildings, Gabalfa, Cardiff (covering Gwent, South, Mid and West Glamorgan); telephone Cardiff (0222) 62131.

Government Buildings, Picton Terrace, Carmarthen, Dyfed (covering Dyfed); telephone Carmarthen (0267) 4545.

The Lindens, Spa Road, Llandrindod Wells, Powys (covering Powys); telephone Llandrindod Wells (0597) 2771.

Station Road, Ruthin, Clwyd (covering Clwyd); telephone Ruthin (082 42) 2611.

❧ *Local Inspectors of the Wine Standards Board of the Vintners' Company*

68 Upper Thames Street, London EC4; telephone 01-236 9512.

The names, addresses and telephone numbers of the inspectors, with their areas of responsibility are given below.

SCOTLAND AND THE BORDER COUNTIES

Mr A. A. Brack, 17 Lockharton Gardens, Edinburgh EH14 1AU: telephone 031-443 3071.
Scotland, Cumbria, Northumberland, Tyne and Wear.

NORTHERN

Mr P. D. Lamming, 13 Park Drive, Harrogate, North Yorkshire; telephone Harrogate (0423) 55155.
Durham, Cleveland, North Yorkshire, West Yorkshire, South Yorkshire, Humberside, Lancashire, Greater Manchester, Merseyside.

WALES AND WEST MIDLANDS

Mr H. C. Perkins, 45 Erdington Road, Aldridge, Walsall, West Midlands; telephone Walsall (0922) 53877.
Wales, Cheshire, Derbyshire, Staffordshire, Salop, Hereford and Worcester, West Midlands, Warwickshire.

EASTERN

Mr C. F. Ball, 12 Rushmere Way, Rushden, Northants; telephone Rushden (093 34) 2779.
Lincolnshire, Nottinghamshire, Leicester, Cambridgeshire, Norfolk, Suffolk, Northamptonshire, Bedfordshire, Hertfordshire, North Essex (down to a line through Harlow, Chelmsford and Maldon all inclusive).

SOUTH-WEST

Mr D. W. Applegate, The Old Kennels, Semington, Trowbridge, Wilts;
telephone Keevil (038 087) 339.
*Cornwall, Devon, Somerset, Dorset, Wiltshire, Avon, Gloucestershire, Oxfordshire,
Hampshire, Isle of Wight, West Berkshire (up to, but excluding Reading).*

LONDON AND SOUTH-EAST (EASTERN AREA)

Mr J. E. Ruberry, 34 Beckenham Court, The Avenue, Beckenham Kent;
telephone 01-650 2532.
*South Essex (below the line Harlow–Chelmsford–Maldon all exclusive), Kent, the
London boroughs of Havering, Barking, Redbridge, Newham, Waltham Forest,
Haringay, Hackney, Tower Hamlets, Islington, the City of London.*

LONDON AND SOUTH-EAST (SOUTHERN AREA)

Mr B. S. R. Penney, 1 Eldred Avenue, Brighton, East Sussex; telephone
Brighton (0273) 552647.
*East Sussex, West Sussex, Surrey, the London boroughs of Bromley, Bexley, Green-
wich, Lewisham, Southwark, Croydon, Sutton, Merton, Lambeth, Wandsworth,
Kingston upon Thames, Richmond upon Thames.*

LONDON AND SOUTH EAST (WESTERN AREA)

Mr H. B. Pickin, 145 Fairlands Avenue, Thornton Heath, Surrey, telephone
01-684 1914.
*Buckinghamshire, East Berkshire (up to Reading), the London boroughs of Hounslow,
Hillingdon, Ealing, Harrow, Brent, Hammersmith, Kensington and Chelsea,
City of Westminster, Camden, Barnet, Enfield.*

NORTHERN IRELAND

Mr C. W. Wyness, 75 Abbey Park, Bangor, County Down, Northern Ireland;
telephone Bangor (0247) 3118.

❧ *Glossary*

Air drainage.   Unimpeded downward flow of cold air.

Anthracnose (or black spot).   Fungal disease controlled by copper fungicides such as zineb.

Armillaria.   Root fungus which can attack vines.

Authorized varieties.   Varieties authorized for cultivation by EEC regulations for the production of 'table wine'.

Bentonite.   A substance used for clarifying wine.

Black spot.   See anthracnose.

Botrytis (or grey mould).   A fungus which rots the grapes and in severe cases can virtually destroy the crop. It can be controlled by certain fungicides and good husbandry.

Burette.   A graduated glass tube for measuring small quantities of liquid.

Campden tablets.   Chemical used for sterilization in winemaking.

Carboy.   Vessel, usually of glass, in which wine is fermented.

Cep.   Stem of vine.

Chaptalization.   Addition of sugar to must.

Chlorosis.   A disease, due to soil deficiencies, in which the green parts of the plant lose their colour and growth is poor.

Clarifying.   Clearing wine which has failed to clear naturally.

Clone.   Cultivar descended from one individual plant.

Cordon (permanent).   A method of pruning which leaves permanent horizontal canes; the fruit is produced on laterals cut back to spurs.

Cordon (semi-permanent).   A variation of the permanent cordon in which two or more of the canes can be replaced each year.

Coulure.   Condition of vine in which grapes form but do not grow.

Crosses.   Vines which are produced by crossing pure-bred European vines.

Day-degrees.   Explained on pages 10–11.

Dead arm.   See phomopsis.

Downy mildew.   See plasmopara.

Époque.   French classification of vines according to their dates of ripening.

Experimental varieties.   Vines which are neither recommended nor authorized by EEC regulations but are allowed to be grown on an experimental basis. In the UK these can be planted in all vineyards. In other EEC states they are only permitted in research stations.

Fermentation lock.   A device which allows carbon dioxide to escape from the fermenting wine without allowing air or impurities in.

Fining.   The clearing of wine.

Frost pocket.   A 'pool' where heavy cold air collects, liable to frosts.

Geneva Double Curtain.   High-culture method of training vines, developed in America.

Goblet pruning.   A method of training which shapes the vine into a bush, with fruit borne on six laterals tied to one central stake.

Grafted vine.   A vine growing on a rootstock.

Grey mould.   See botrytis.

Guillage.   A system of fermentation in which the vessel·is filled to the top to allow debris and dirt to be thrown out by the violence of the fermenting must.

Guyot system.   A method devised by Dr Jules Guyot of increasing yield and quality of fruit by severely restricting the growth of the vine and tying down the fruiting cane or canes, which may number one (single Guyot), two (double Guyot) or four (double-double Guyot). These are cut down and replaced by new canes each year.

Hâtif.   Vines which require a shorter than usual period between flowering and ripening.

High culture.   Growing vines high with the bottom wire at least 650 mm (2 ft 1½ ins) from the ground. In some systems the bottom wire is set 1.8 m (6 feet) above ground.

Hybrid vine.   Vine produced by artificial pollination between an American vine and *Vitis vinifera* (European vine).

Hydrometer.   A measuring instrument which, when floated in a liquid, measures its density; used to give readings of the sugar content of grape juice.

Lateral.   A shoot growing out from the main cane or canes.

Lees.   Sediment from fermenting wine.

Lenz Moser.   High-culture method of training vines developed by Dr Lenz Moser in Austria.

Low culture.   Growing vines low with the bottom wire not more than 500 mm (1 ft 8 ins) from the ground.

Milling.   Crushing of grapes prior to pressing.

Must.   Wine before fermentation; pressed grape juice.

Oechsle degrees (°Oe).   Scale for measuring sugar content of grape juice.

Oidium (or powdery mildew).   A disease of vines caused by the fungus, *Uncinula necator*, which can be controlled by sulphur.

Oxidation.   Chemical changes in wine, due to exposure to the air, which destroy the flavour.

Penicillium.   Green fungus (*P. crustaceum*) which often accompanies botrytis.

Peronospora.   Name formerly used for downy mildew (*Plasmopara viticula*). See plasmopara.

Phomopsis.   A fungus which causes the disease called dead arm, which can kill branches or even a whole vine if untreated.

Phylloxera.   An insect which attacks the roots of vines and kills all vines except those on resistant rootstocks. Endemic in Europe but not in Britain.

Pipette.   Tube for removing an accurately measured small quantity of liquid.

Plasmopara.   Fungus which causes downy mildew.

Pomace.   Pulpy residue from a wine press.

Potassium metabisulphate.   Chemical used for sterilization in winemaking.

Pourriture grise (grey rot).   A grey mould. An early form of botrytis, very damaging to the harvest. See botrytis.

Pourriture noble (the noble rot).   A late form of botrytis, rare in Britain, which concentrates the sugar content of the grapes.

Powdery mildew.   See oidium.

Precipitated chalk.   A substance sometimes added to wine to counteract acidity.

Précoce.   Early flowering vines.

Première époque.   First early vines (see époque).

Protected variety.   Vine developed by a breeder which must not be reproduced without his permission.

Racking.   Siphoning wine from one container to another.

Recommended varieties.   Those recommended for cultivation by EEC regulations. Wines from these varieties only are entitled to be considered as 'quality wines'.

Refractometer.   Small instrument for measuring the sugar content of grape juice from a drop of the juice.

Relative density (or specific gravity).   Ratio of the density of a substance to that of water at the same temperature.

Rooted cutting.   A young vine growing on its own roots.

Rootstock.   A cutting, providing roots, on to which another variety can be grafted.

Scion.   A vine cutting which is grafted on to a rootstock.

Sodium metabisulphate.   Chemical used in winemaking for sterilization.

Specific gravity.   See relative density.

Spur pruning.   Pruning for fruit bearing on short lateral shoots or spurs.

Spurs.   Fruit-bearing lateral shoots, pruned short on permanent or semi-permanent branches.

Stocks.   See rootstocks.

Sublateral.   Shoot growing out of a lateral shoot (see lateral).

Sulphiting.   Sterilizing with sulphur dioxide to destroy unwanted yeasts and impurities.

Systemic pesticide.   Chemical absorbed by a plant which makes the plant poisonous to pests.

Titration.   Method of measuring acidity of grape juice.

Trellis.   Post and wire support for vines.

Véraison.   Stage when the ripening grapes begin to change colour.

Vinification.   The making of wine.

Viticulture.   The cultivation of vines.

Vitis labrusca.   An American vine.

Vitis riperia.   An American vine.

Vitis rupestris.   An American vine.

Vitis vinifera.   Native European vine.

Yeast casse.   Unpleasant flavour in the wine due to leaving it too long without racking after fermentation.

Yeast starter.   Wine yeast added to small quantity of sterilized grape juice and kept in a warm place for two or three days to start off fermentation in a larger quantity.

Index